Liquid Membranes

Liquid Membranes
Theory and Applications

Richard D. Noble, EDITOR
National Bureau of Standards

J. Douglas Way, EDITOR
National Bureau of Standards

Developed from a symposium presented at
the 8th Rocky Mountain Regional Meeting
of the American Chemical Society
in Denver, Colorado,
June 8–12, 1986

American Chemical Society, Washington, DC 1987

Library of Congress Cataloging-in-Publication Data

Liquid membranes.
  (ACS symposium series, 0097-6156; 347)

  "Developed from a symposium presented at
the 8th Rocky Mountain Regional Meeting of the
American Chemical Society in Denver, Colorado,
June 8-12, 1986."

  Includes bibliographies and indexes.

  1. Liquid membranes—Congresses.

  I. Noble, R. D. (Richard D.), 1946-   . II. Way,
J. Douglas. III. American Chemical Society.
IV. American Chemical Society. Rocky Mountain
Regional Meeting (8th: 1986: Denver, Colo.) V. Series.

QD562.I63L57   1987   660.2'842   87-18684
ISBN 0-8412-1407-7

ACS Symposium Series

M. Joan Comstock, *Series Editor*

1987 Advisory Board

Foreword

The ACS SYMPOSIUM SERIES was founded in 1974 to provide a medium for publishing symposia quickly in book form. The format of the Series parallels that of the continuing ADVANCES IN CHEMISTRY SERIES except that, in order to save time, the papers are not typeset but are reproduced as they are submitted by the authors in camera-ready form. Papers are reviewed under the supervision of the Editors with the assistance of the Series Advisory Board and are selected to maintain the integrity of the symposia; however, verbatim reproductions of previously published papers are not accepted. Both reviews and reports of research are acceptable, because symposia may embrace both types of presentation.

Contents

Preface

LIQUID MEMBRANE TECHNOLOGY is coming of age. The chapters in this book indicate the renewed and widespread activity in this field. This renaissance has come about because of the following factors: better understanding of carrier chemistry for carrier-mediated transport, better support materials such as ion-exchange membranes, an increasing number of applications, and better predictive capabilities. Commercialization of this technology for both gas- and liquid-phase separations within the past year indicates its highly advanced status. To keep this technology growing, the objective of this book is to present state-of-the-art papers on various aspects of this technology that can assist either the novice or practitioner. The text covers liquid- and gas-phase separation, emulsion and immobilized liquid membranes, theory, experimentation, and applications.

Putting this book together has been particularly satisfying for us because, as the saying goes, the time is right. The increased activity in the field coincides with the completion of the text. Our timing was fortuitous and a little lucky. We have also been fortunate to get the authors to contribute their work and add to the ultimate success of this book. This book was also completed in spite of a six-month sabbatical in Italy (R.D.N.) and a job change (J.D.W.). Our desire to turn out a good piece of work overcame these and other obstacles. We hope that, after you use the book, you agree that the effort was worthwhile.

A special thanks to Susan Robinson and the ACS Books Department staff for a job well done. An excellent typing performance was accomplished by Terry Yenser and Vicky Vivoda of the Word Processing group at the National Bureau of Standards.

We also acknowledge the support of Madhav Ghate and Lisa Jarr of Morgantown Energy Technology Center through DOE Contract No. DE-AI21-86MC23120.

RICHARD D. NOBLE
National Bureau of Standards
Center for Chemical Engineering
Boulder, CO 80303

J. DOUGLAS WAY
SRI International
Chemical Engineering Laboratory
Menlo Park, CA 94025

May 1987

Chapter 1

Liquid Membrane Technology
An Overview

Richard D. Noble and J. Douglas Way[1]

National Bureau of Standards, Center for Chemical Engineering, Boulder, CO 80303

Liquid membrane technology is introduced and is identified as a subset of membrane science. A tutorial section discusses configurations, transport mechanisms,
experimental techniques, and a survey of basic theoretical approaches. The concepts of reactive liquid membranes which combine traditional unit operations such
as extraction or absorption with stripping are discussed. The chapters to follow in this volume are summarized and the subject of each is placed in perspective
to the field of liquid membrane technology.

Tutorial

A membrane can be viewed as a semi-permeable barrier between two
phases. This barrier can restrict the movement of molecules across
it in a very specific manner. The membrane must act as a barrier
between phases to prevent intimate contact. The semi-permeable nature is essential to insuring that a separation takes place.
There are two points to note concerning this definition.
First, a membrane is defined based on what it does, not what it is.
Secondly, a membrane separation is a rate process. The separation
is accomplished by a driving force, not by equilibrium between
phases (1).
By extending our definition of a membrane, we can include liquids. If we view a membrane as a semipermeable barrier between two
phases, then an immiscible liquid can serve as a membrane between
two liquid or gas phases. Different solutes will have different
solubilities and diffusion coefficients in a liquid. The product of
these two terms is a measure of the permeability. A liquid can yield
selective permeabilities and, therefore, a separation. Because the
diffusion coefficients in liquids are typically orders of magnitude
higher than in polymers, a larger flux can be obtained.

[1]Current address: SRI International, Chemical Engineering Laboratory,
Menlo Park, CA 94025

Liquid membranes can be prepared in two different configurations (see fig. 1). A liquid can be impregnated in the pores of a porous solid for mechanical support. This form is commonly known as an immobilized liquid membrane (ILM). In the alternate configuration, the receiving phase is emulsified in an immiscible liquid membrane. This type of liquid membrane is known as a liquid surfactant, or emulsion liquid membrane (ELM).

An ILM can be made in at least three different geometries. A planar or flat geometry is very useful for laboratory purposes. For industrial purposes a planar geometry is not very effective since the ratio of surface area to volume is too low. Hollow fiber and spiral wound modules can be used to provide high surface area to volume ratios. Surface area to volume ratios can approach 10,000 m^2/m^3 for hollow fiber and 1000 m^2/m^3 for spiral wound modules (2). Way et al. (3) discuss the criteria for selecting supports for ILMs.

There are two primary problems associated with the use of ILMs. Solvent loss can occur. This loss is caused by evaporation, dissolution, or large pressure differences forcing solvent out of the pore support structure. Also, carrier loss can occur. This loss can be due to irreversible side reactions or solvent condensation on one side of the membrane. Pressure differences can force the liquid to flow through the pore structure and leach out the carrier.

Ion exchange membranes (IEMs) have recently been studied as a means for overcoming the above problems (4). The carrier is the counter ion in the IEM. The carrier is bound in the membrane by ionic charge forces. The IEM is a nonporous polymer which is swelled by the solvent. Because the IEM is nonporous, no "short circuiting" occurs if the membrane loses solvent. The carrier also remains bound in the membrane. The membrane can be resolvated and continue performing without a loss in capacity

Emulsion liquid membranes are also known as double emulsions. Two immiscible phases are mixed with a surfactant to produce an emulsion. This emulsion is then dispersed in a continuous phase. Mass transfer takes place between the continuous phase and the inner phase through the immiscible (membrane) phase. Figure 1 shows both an ILM and an ELM.

In both purification and recovery applications the ELM must be demulsified into two immiscible phases after the extraction step of the process. This is commonly accomplished by heating, application of electric fields (5), or centrifugation. The liquid membrane phase containing the surfactant and carrier will be recycled to the emulsion preparation step while the internal phase of the emulsion containing the concentrated solute will undergo further purification in a recovery process or treatment and disposal in a purification process. Such a continuous process is shown in Figure 2.

The major problem associated with ELMs is emulsion stability. The emulsion must be formulated to withstand the shear generated by mixing during the extraction but must be broken to remove the internal phase and reformulate the emulsion. This requires an additional process step and additional energy inputs. Consequently, this process has limited potential applications to recovery of products with high added value or to pollution control, where process efficiency and degree of separation may be more important than the cost of the process.

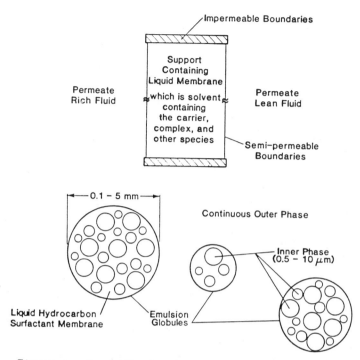

Figure 1.   Immobilized and emulsion liquid membranes. (Reproduced from Ref. 23.)

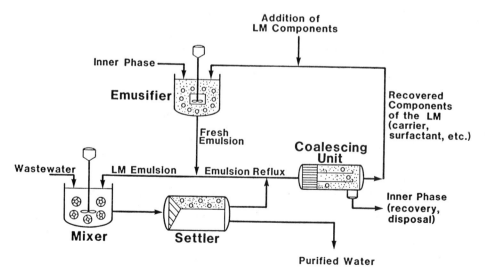

Figure 2.   Flowsheet of an emulsion liquid membrane extraction process.

improvements

As stated above, the use of a liquid phase can enhance the solute flux due to the higher diffusion coefficients in liquids than in
solids. Further enhancement can be accomplished by using a nonvolatile carrier in the liquid (6). This carrier molecule can selectively and reversibly react with the solute. This reversible reaction
provides a means of enhancing the solute flux and improving the selectivity at the same time. There are two basic mechanisms for this
enhanced transport. In coupled transport the reversible reaction is
an ion exchange, and the solute flux is linked (coupled) to the exchange ion flux (see Fig. 3a). The carrier is an ion exchange reagent. This reaction normally occurs at a liquid-liquid interface
since the ions are not soluble in an organic phase. Facilitated
transport is concerned with the reversible reaction between the solute and carrier and is not coupled to other components. This reaction normally can take place throughout the liquid membrane phase
(see fig. 2b). Variations on these reaction schemes are possible
and are described in a recent paper by Goddard (7).
        Four points demonstrate the benefits of using carriers in liq-
uid membranes.

1.   High fluxes are possible. By combining the advantages of high
     diffusion coefficients in liquids with the added carrying
     capacity of the carrier, larger fluxes than in polymer membranes
     are possible.
2.   Very selective separations are possible. The selective nature
     of the carrier provides much better separations than those
     obtainable based solely on relative solubility and diffusion.
3.   Ions can be concentrated. Coupled transport allows one to pump
     ions against their concentration gradient.
4.   Expensive extractants can be used. Small amounts of carrier are
     used because of the small solvent inventory associated with the
     membrane and because of the nonvolatile nature of the carrier.

        There are related fields of study which potentially can have an
impact on carrier-mediated membrane separations. The reader may
wish to explore these topics for details on some aspect of the specific system of interest. These fields include:

a)   Conventional solvent extraction. Many solvent-extractive agent
     systems are transferable to liquid membranes.
b)   Gas absorption. Same point as a).
c)   Phase transfer catalysis. Many carrier-solvent systems,
     especially those for ion transport, are discussed under this
     topic. A good reference is Dehmlow and Dehmlow (8).
d)   Biological systems. Many biological processes involve "active"
     or carrier-mediated transport. Two examples are oxygen
     transport and nerve signal transmission. A good reference for
     biological membrane systems is Fendler (9).
e)   Guest-host chemistry. One subgroup of this area is inclusion
     phenomena. Many possible carriers would be included in this
     area, although at present most work in this area has not focused
     on reversibility.
f)   Interfacial phenomena. This area is important for liquid-liquid
     systems. This topic includes interfacial kinetics. Many

carrier-solute reactions occur at the interface for liquid-
liquid systems. A recent review article discusses the
various methods for measuring interfacial kinetics (10).
g) Dispersed phase systems. ELM systems fall within this category.
h) Membrane reactors. A recent development is the use of composite
   membrane layers to perform reactions as well as separations.
   Liquid membranes can form part or all of the membrane layers.

There have been previous review articles that cover various
aspects of liquid membrane separations. The reader is referred to
them for further information (11-23).

Experimental Methods

Immobilized Liquid Membranes. Facilitated transport liquid membranes for gas separations can be prepared in several configurations.
The complexation agent solution can be held between two nonporous
polymer films (24), impregnated into the pore structure of a microporous polymer film (25), or the carrier can be exchanged for the
counterion in an ion exchange membrane (4).
    In studies of NO facilitated transport, Ward (24) immobilized a
formamide solution of Fe^{2+} ions between two silicone rubber membranes. Ward's analysis of the mass transfer data from the liquid
membrane cell showed that the resistance of the silicone rubber supporting membranes was negligible compaired to the resistance of the
0.1 cm formamide liquid membrane. Ward (26) used an identical membrane configuration to study electrically induced facilitated gas
transport. A similar immobilization technique was used by Otto and
Quinn (27) to prepare an ILM for CO_2 transport. An aqueous bicarbonate solution was immobilized between silicone copolymer membranes
formulated to have high CO_2 permeability (28).
    The most widely used approach to prepare ILMs has been to im-
pregnate the pore structure of a thin, microporous substrate such as
an ultrafiltration membrane with the liquid containing the complexation agent. Figure 4 illustrates a typical ILM cross-section.
Many different supports have been used to prepare ILMs including
cellulose acetate reverse osmosis membranes (16, 25, 29, 30), microporous polypropylene ultrafiltration membranes (31-34), polyvinyl
chloride filters (35), and hollow fiber cellulose acetate reverse
osmosis membranes (36). Way et al. (3) discuss the chemical and
physical properties that must be considered when an ILM support is
selected.
    However, immobilized liquid membranes supported with porous
substrates have two primary experimental problems: loss of solvent
and loss or deactivation of the carrier. Matson et al. (30) prevent-
ed evaporative loss of liquid by maintaining the relative humidity
of the gas streams in the range of 60 to 90%. Another problem may
arise when humidification is used. If solvent condenses out of the
feed gas stream onto the ILM and a pressure gradient between the
feed and sweep gas stream exists, solvent may flow through the support pore structure leaching the carrier out of the membrane.
Kimura et al. (16) noted that a major problem was maintaining the
integrity of the supported liquid membrane when large pressure differences were imposed across the membrane.

A + CB ⇌ CA + B (interfacial reaction)

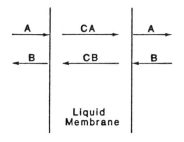

A + B ⇌ AB (homogeneous reaction)

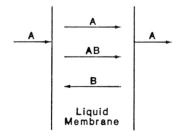

Figure 3. Examples of coupled and facilitated transport. (Reproduced from Ref. 23.)

FEED PHASE

Liquid membrane phase
containing solvent and
complexing agent

Porous Support

RECEIVING PHASE

Figure 4. Cross section of an immobilized membrane. (Reproduced from Ref. 23.)

A promising recent approach used to prepare facilitated transport membranes is to use an ion exchange membrane as a support for a complexation agent (4, 37). An ionically charged complexation agent is exchanged for the counterion in cation or anion exchange membranes. This configuration has the advantage that the carrier cannot easily be forced or washed out of the membrane since the carrier is retained by electrostatic forces. This approach could provide a longer useful operating life.

ILM Gas Flux Measurement. Several methods have been used to measure fluxes through ILMs: a transient pressure measurement (24), a radioisotope tracer technique (38), and a flow cell technique (30, 34).

In his measurements of NO facilitated transport, Ward (24), used a capacitance manometer to measure the pressure buildup on the low pressure (product) side of the membrane cell. Steady state values of the mass flux through the membrane were calculated from the rate of pressure increase.

Donaldson and Quinn (38) reported the development of a ^{14}C tracer method of flux measurement in studies of CO_2 transport. Both sides of an ILM containing a $KHCO_3$ carrier species were equilibrated with untagged gas. A small quantity of isotopic tracer was introduced into one side of the membrane cell and the diffusion rate of the tagged species was measured. Their studies of the kinetics of the CO_2-$HCO_3{}^{2-}$ reaction with and without the enzyme carbonic anhydrase were greatly simplified by the fact that negligible pH gradients were established during the measurements. Under these conditions the reaction rate expressions were first order, removing the nonlinearities from the governing differential equations.

Matson et al. (30) designed a flow system for measurements of H_2S permeability through ILMs at temperatures of 363-403 K and total feed pressures of 2.1×10^3 kPa. The ILM consisted of a 30 wt. % K_2CO_3 aqueous solution immobilized in microporous cellulose acetate and polyether sulfone films. The feed gas, a mixture of H_2S, CO_2, and N_2 was humidified and sent to a temperature controlled membrane cell. A helium sweep gas was similarly humidified and served to carry the permeating gases to analysis by gas chromatography.

Bateman et al. (34) discuss in detail a membrane gas flow system and cell used for the measurement of gas fluxes through facilitated transport membranes. As shown in figure 5, a feed gas with up to four components can be humidified and delivered to the membrane cell. An inert sweep gas, typically He, is humidified and sent to the other side of the membrane cell. Solvents in the gas streams are removed in a cold trap downstream of the membrane cell prior to analysis by gas chromatography. An exploded view of the facilitated transport membrane cell is shown in figure 6. The analog signal from the chromatography detector is integrated and sent to a laboratory microcomputer which calculates flux and selectivities from the concentration data. This system has been successfully used with several different carrier-gas systems including NO, CO, CO_2, and H_2S. Due to the toxic and corrosive nature of several of these gases, the entire system was fabricated of stainless steel, glass, and polytetrafluoroethylene.

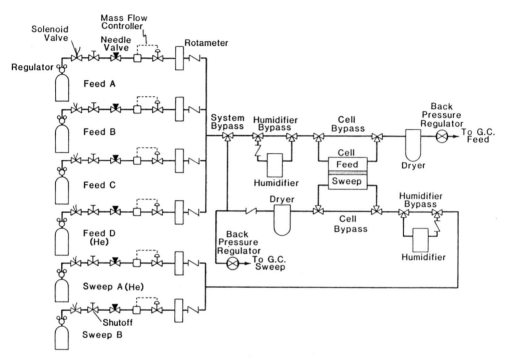

Figure 5.   Schematic of membrane transport apparatus.
(Reproduced from Ref. 23.)

Emulsion or Liquid Surfactant Membranes.   Several review articles
have surveyed emulsion liquid membrane technology (17, 20).   As
shown in Figure 1, liquid surfactant or emulsion liquid membranes
(ELM) consist of an inner receiving phase dispersed in an immiscible
liquid membrane phase to form an emulsion and stabilized by surfactants with appropriate hydrophilic-lipophilic balance (HLB) number
(39).   The HLB is a parameter which is the percentage of hydrophilic
functional groups in the surfactant molecule divided by five.   A
hypothetical surfactant having only hydrophilic character would have
an HLB value of 20.   The liquid membrane phase can be either aqueous
or organic although the majority of work in the literature describes
water in oil emulsions.   In facilitated or coupled transport, a carrier species is incorporated into the liquid membrane phase.
    Kopp (40) created a set of guidelines for the formation of
stable water in oil ELMs:

    a. Organic phase soluble surfactant concentration, 0.1 to
        5 wt. %
    b. Organic phase viscosity, 30 to 1000 mPa·s
    c. Volume ratio of the internal receiving phase to membrane
        phase, 0.2 to 2.0
    d. Volume ratio of internal phase to continuous external
        phase, 0.2 to 0.05
    e. Volume ratio continuous phase to emulsion phase, 1 to 40
    f. Surfactant HLB value, 6 to 8

Frankenfeld et al. (41) discussed the effect of many of these parameters on the performance of an ELM for Cu^{2+} extraction.
    In use, the ELM is dispersed in a continuous phase and sepa-
rates two miscible phases.   Under agitation, the ELM phase separates
into spherical globules of emulsion which have typical diameters of
10 μm to 1 mm.   Each globule contains many droplets of encapsulated
inner or receiving phase with a typical size of 1 to 10 μm in diameter.   The formation of many globules of emulsion produces large
surface area/volume ratios of 1000 to 3000 m^2/m^3 for very rapid mass
transfer (20).   Due to this dispersed emulsion configuration, ELMs
or liquid surfactant membranes are commonly referred to as double
emulsions.
    The transport of a solute from the continuous phase to the in-
ner receiving phase can occur by a variety of mechanisms as shown in
Figure 7.
    The constituents of the ELM for extraction of a solute must be
chosen in such a way that once the solute diffuses into the inner
receiving phase it cannot diffuse back out into the continuous phase.
Often, ionic solutes such as metal ions are not soluble in the organic liquid membrane phase.   For nonionic solutes such as organic
acids, this can be accomplished by the use of a trapping reaction in
the internal phase, such as reacting phenol with NaOH.   This creates
an ionic species, sodium phenolate, which is insoluble in the liquid
membrane phase.

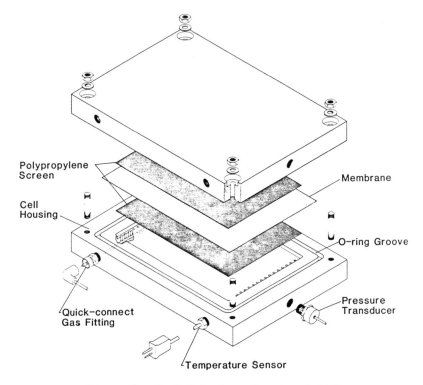

Figure 6.   Exploded view of membrane cell.
(Reproduced from Ref. 23.)

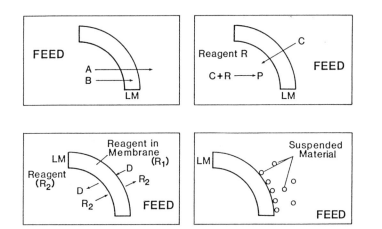

Figure 7.   Various liquid membrane transport mechanisms.
(Reproduced with permission from Ref. 41.   Copyright 1981, Dekker.)

Modeling

The mathematical modeling of liquid membrane separations is essential to accurate prediction and scale-up of these systems. Also, accurate and complete models identify the important physical properties and operating conditions. Models can be used to identify and guide the pertinent experimental program which should be followed.

Immobilized Liquid Membranes. Many of the early studies on liquid membranes dealt with immobilized liquid membranes. Therefore, a large amount of modeling describes these systems. Also, many of the modeling efforts have focused on facilitated transport where a nonvolatile carrier is present in the membrane. The reaction scheme most often used is A+B = AB where A is the solute to be separated, B is the nonvolatile carrier, and AB is the carrier-solute complex. In such a system, the parameters which affect system performance are a) the total carrier concentration (C_T), b) the solute concentration on each side of the membrane (C_{AO} = feed, C_{AL} = sweep), c) the forward and reverse rate constants (k_1 and k_2 respectively), d) the membrane thickness (L), and e) the diffusion coefficients of the three components in the liquid membrane (D_A, D_B, and D_{AB}).
The major output of interest is the solute flux through the liquid membrane. Often, this flux is described in a dimensionless fashion as a facilitation factor (F). F is defined as the total solute flux with carrier present divided by the diffusional flux of solute alone.
The above parameters can be cast into three dimensionless variables (see Table 1). ε is the inverse of a Damkohler number and gives a measure of the relationship between the characteristic reverse reaction and diffusion times. A small value of ε indicates reaction equilibrium (diffusion-limited) and a large value indicates a reaction-limited case. K is a dimensionless equilibrium constant. Kemena et al. (42) describe the optimal values of this variable. α is a mobility ratio between carrier and solute. α is directly proportional to the initial carrier concentration so it is a measure of increasing or decreasing the amount of carrier present.
Early modeling efforts focused on equilibrium and near equilibrium conditions. Olander (43) developed analytical solutions for a variety of reaction shemes under reaction equilibrium conditions. Friedlander and Keller (44) used an affinity function to obtain analytical solutions for systems near reaction equilibrium. Secor and Beutler (45) used penetration theory to calculate transient mass transfer by numerical methods. Their results for semi-infinite media can be used for short time results.
Some analytical solutions have been developed. Ward (24) was able to develop analytical solutions for the solute flux under both diffusion-limited and reaction-limited conditions. These solutions provide upper and lower limits, respectively, on the solute flux. In terms of the above variables, the diffusion-limited solution is:

$$F = 1 + \frac{\alpha \, K}{(1 + K)} \qquad (1)$$

Table 1. Dimensionless Variables

$\varepsilon = \dfrac{D_{AB}}{k_2 L^2}$		= inverse Damkohler number
$K = \dfrac{k_1}{k_2}\left(C_{AO}\right)$		= dimensionless reaction equilibrium constant
$\alpha = \dfrac{D_{AB}}{D_A}\dfrac{C_T}{C_{AO}}$		= mobility ratio (ratio of mobility of carrier to mobility of permeate)
$Sh = \dfrac{kL}{D_A}$		= Sherwood number for permeate mass transfer
k		= mass transfer coefficient based on concentration driving force

Smith and Quinn (35) and Hoofd and Kreuzer (46) independently developed analytical solutions for the facilitation factor which holds over a range in properties and operating conditions. Smith and Quinn obtained their solution by assuming a large excess of carrier. This allowed them to linearize the resulting differential equations. Hoofd and Kreuzer separated their solution into two parts: a reaction-limited portion which is valid near the interface and a diffusion-limited portion within the membrane. Both groups obtained the same result for the facilitation factor. Hoofd and Kreuzer (47) then extended their approach to cylinders and spheres. Recently, Noble et al. (48) developed an analytical solution for F based on flux boundary conditions. This solution allows for external mass transfer resistance and reduces to the Smith and Quinn equation in the limit as the Sherwood number (Sh) becomes very large.

$$F = \frac{\left[1 + \dfrac{\alpha K}{(1 + K)}\right]\left[1 + \dfrac{1}{Sh_O} + \dfrac{1}{Sh_L}\right]}{1 + \dfrac{\alpha K}{(1 + K)}\dfrac{\tanh \lambda}{\lambda} + \left[1 + \dfrac{\alpha K}{(1 + K)}\right]\left[\dfrac{1}{Sh_O} + \dfrac{1}{Sh_L}\right]} \qquad (2)$$

$$\text{where } \lambda = 1/2 \left[\frac{1 + (\alpha + 1)K}{\varepsilon (1 + K)}\right]^{\frac{1}{2}} \qquad (3)$$

Way et al. (37) applied this analytical model to predict facilitation factors for CO_2 facilitated transport in ion exchange membranes. As shown in Figure 8, there was good agreement between experimental and predicted facilitation factors.

The above solutions are constrained to steady state conditions, one dimensional transport, and a single solute. Cussler (49) derived an analytical expression for the solute flux when two solutes compete for a single carrier. His simplified analysis demonstrated that it is possible to "pump" one solute against its concentration gradient.

Noble (50) extended the one dimensional solution for facilitated transport to obtain an analytical solution for solute flux through a hollow fiber membrane. This result allows for convective transport through the lumen and radial transport through the membrane walls. The solution can also be used with planar geometry and

no facilitation. Teremoto et al. (51) modeled copper extraction
(coupled transport) through hollow fiber membranes.

Limiting solutions based on pertubation methods have also been
discussed in the literature. Goddard et al. (52), Kreuzer and Hoofd
(53), and Smith et al. (54) all used matched asymptotic expansions
to develop criteria for reactive boundary layer zones within facilitated transport membranes. These results can also be used to calculate solute fluxes. For systems of interest, the reaction boundary
layer will be negligible and an analysis of this detail is unnecessary.

When the simplifying assumptions used for developing analytical
solutions are no longer valid, it is necessary to employ numerical
methods because the equations are inherently nonlinear. Several
authors have used different numerical methods to analyze facilitated
transport using the reaction scheme described in the beginning of
this section. Suchdeo and Schultz (55) used a quasilinearization
technique to obtain solutions when diffusion or reaction were not
controlling. Yung and Probstein (56) used a similarity transforma-
tion to obtain a single nonlinear differential equation for the concentration profiles across the membrane. Their result can be used
to calculate the facilitation factor. Jain and Schultz (57) described a collocation technique which will also provide the concentration profiles and the facilitation factor. Their analysis is
more complex than that of Yung and Probstein. Folkner and Noble
(58) extended the above results to also account for transient
effects. Their results converged to the same steady-state results
as previous models. Niiya and Noble (59) extended previous models
to include competitive effects of two solutes for a single carrier
under both transient and steady state conditions. Their model also
allows for external mass transfer resistance.

Way (60) applied the competitive transport model of Niiya and
Noble (59) to the prediction of facilitation factors for competitive
transport of CO_2 and H_2S in ion exchange membranes containing organic amine carriers. The results of the numerical simulations are
shown in Table 2. The agreement is very good for CO_2 and qualita-
tive for H_2S.

The reaction between the solute and carrier in facilitated
transport must be delicately balanced to provide a large increase in
solute flux. If the carrier and solute are strongly bound, solute
will be slowly released at the downstream side of the membrane.
This results in large numbers of carrier sites being occupied for
longer times than required for transport across the membrane. Alter-
nately, very little facilitation takes place when the solute and
carrier are weakly bound. Schultz et al. (11) developed an analytical equation for the optimum equilibrium constant under reaction
equilibrium conditions. Kemena et al. (42) numerically determined
the optimum equilibrium constant under a wide range of conditions.
As shown in Figure 9, for orders of magnitude change in the carrier
concentration and membrane thickness, they found that their dimensionless equilibrium constant ranged only between 1 and 10. Their
result provides a useful method to screen potential carriers and
also to determine the comparison between actual and optimum performance. Noble (61) recently defined a kinetic efficiency factor.

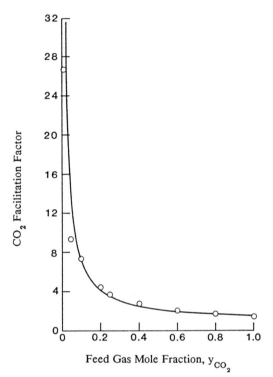

Figure 8. Comparison of predicted carbon dioxide facilitation
factors to experimental data.

Table 2. Comparison of Experimental Facilitation Factors
for Competitive Transport with Theory

Feed Y		F_{CO_2}		F_{H_2S}	
H_2S	CO_2	Exp	Theory	Exp	Theory
0.01	0.08	9.11	8.72	~1.0	1.08
0.02	0.06	16.0	13.0	1.81	1.13
0.05	0.05	16.7	16.8	1.80	1.17
0.02	0.05	18.0	17.3	1.56	1.18
0.03	0.04	20.6	19.9	2.13	1.21
0.04	0.02	26.8	43.8	2.49	1.48

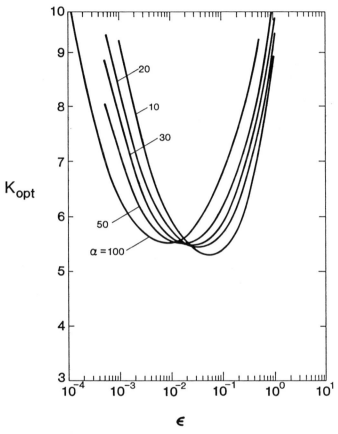

Figure 9. The influence of epsilon on the optimum dimensionless
equilibrium constant for a range of alpha values. (Reproduced
from Ref. 42.)

This factor is similar to an effectiveness factor in catalysis and
provides a measure of diffusion or reaction limited behavior.
    Transient effects have been studied. Spaan (62) modeled oxygen
transport in a stationary film. He used an advancing front hypothe-
sis to measure solute movement through the film. Curl and Schultz
(63) used a polynomial approximation for unsteady-state diffusion of
oxygen into hemoglobin solutions. Their approximation is more general than previous models. Their model reduces to other cases (i.e.
advancing front and linear isotherm cases) when the slope of the
lines represented by the polynomial approximation are varied for the
hemoglobin oxygenation saturation curve. Spaan et al. (64) developed an unsteady-state model for oxygen transport in hemoglobin solutions. Their model assumes chemical equilibrium. Plots of dimensionless oxygenation time versus three dimensionless parameters are
obtained. Folkner and Noble (58) plotted facilitation factor versus
dimensionless time for planar, cylindrical, and spherical geometries.
    Other effects have also been studied. Kemp and Noble (65)
looked at the effect of imposing a temperature gradient across the
membrane. Depending on the temperature effect on the kinetics, this
coupling could cause a significant increase or decrease in the facilitation. Ruckenstein and Sasidhar (66) and Leiber et al. (67)
studied the effect of ionic motion on facilitated transport. Many
carriers are ionic. This effect of ionic motion to create an electrical potential field only becomes significant when there is a
large difference between the carrier and the carrier-solute complex
diffusion coefficients. Recently, Athayde and Ivory (68) reported
on the use of external AC fields to improve the facilitation. Their
results showed that certain frequencies improved the facilitation.
Goddard (69) earlier discussed electric field effects on facilitated
ion transport. The use of light to enhance facilitation has also
been reported (70, 71). Light can affect the rate of reversible
complexation. This effect can be positive or negative depending on
the use. Stroeve and coworkers (72, 73) analyzed the effect of dispersed reactive shapes in a diffusive medium. They plotted facilitation factors for different geometries.
    Danesi and coworkers have developed a model for metal extrac-
tion using supported liquid membranes. Danesi et al. (74) included
both interfacial reaction and boundary layers in their analysis. As
they demonstrate, both effects can be important. Recently, Danesi
(75) developed a simplified model of metal extraction in hollow
fiber membranes based on the model above. Danesi and Reichley-
Yinger (76) have expanded this model to include deviations from a
first order rate law.

Emulsion Liquid Membranes. Emulsion liquid membranes have been
modeled by numerous researchers. Chan and Lee (77) reviewed the
various models. The simplest representation characterizes the emulsion globule (membrane phase) as a spherical shell of constant thickness surrounding a single internal phase droplet. This representation is equivalent to assuming that the membrane and internal phase
are well mixed. In practice, this is usually a poor assumption.
    Kremesec (78) and Kremesec and Slattery (79) used planar geom-
etry and summed mass transfer resistances through each phase in

series. Their method accounts for geometry and internal circulation
effects by using an overall mass transfer coefficient.

Using the spherical shell approach, Cahn and Li (80) modeled
the removal of phenol from wastewater using ELM. They assumed that
the solute transport rate was directly proportional to the solute
concentration difference across the membrane phase. They also assumed that the solute was instantaneously and irreversibly consumed
in the internal phase. Analysis of their experimental results
showed that the effective permeability varied with time. Boyadzhiev
et al. (81) used this same analysis but did not account for internal phase consumption. Gladek et al. (82) allowed the solute partition coefficient to vary with concentration when modeling unsteady-
state solute absorption.

Facilitated or coupled transport in ELMs has also been modeled
using the spherical shell approach. Matulevicius and Li (83) solved
the time dependent mass transfer equations in an attempt to theoretically explain the time dependent permeability for phenol extraction.
They assumed that the solute diffusion through the membrane phase is
the controlling resistance. Hochhauser and Cussler (84) used similar assumptions to analyze chromium concentration using coupled
transport. Way and Noble (85) modeled copper extraction for a continuous stirred tank reactor. They included residence time and
particle size distributions in their analysis. Teremoto et al. (86)
provided a more detailed analysis of copper extraction which included residence time distribution. Noble (87) developed analytical
expressions for shape factors to correct the planar geometry
facilitation factor for cylindrical or spherical geometry under
diffusionlimited or reaction-limited conditions. Folkner and Noble
(58) provide transient solutions for the facilitation factor for
spherical membranes. Stroeve et al. (88) used the combined
Damkohler technique (46) to model facilitated transport in spherical
shell membranes. Their analytical results compared very well with
earlier numerical results.

The spherical shell approach is mathematically simple but fails
to provide accurate results for many systems of interest. Properties such as diffusion coefficients and permeabilities estimated
with the spherical shell approach will vary with extraction. A more
accurate and complex approach is to describe the emulsion globule as
a heterogeneous media. The internal phase droplets are uniformly
dispersed throughout the membrane phase. While the internal droplets have a size distribution, they are small enough compared to the
globule that they can be considered as point sources or sinks.

When reaction occurs in the internal phase, one use of the
above approach is to assume that the solute diffuses through the
globule to a reaction front, where it is removed instantaneously and
irreversibly by reaction with an internal reagent. A reaction front
is formed and proceeds toward the center as the reaction proceeds.

Kopp et al. (89) used this approach to examine the analogous
planar problem with constant bulk solute concentration. Ho et al.
(90), Kim et al. (91) and Stroeve and coworkers (92, 93) formulated
advancing-front models which include both spherical geometry and
depletion of solute in the continuous phase. All three models assume homogeneous distribution of noncirculating internal droplets
within the globule, although Kim et al. assume a thin outer liquid

membrane layer which contains no internal droplets. For globule
diffusion controlling solute transfer, Ho et al. used a perturbation
method to solve the resulting system of nonlinear equations. They
determined that the zero order or pseudosteady state solution was
sufficient to calculate phenol removal from the continuous phase as
a function of time. Using a Sauter mean diameter for the average
globule size and no adjustable parameters, they predicted somewhat
higher removal rates than observed experimentally. Stroeve and
Varanasi use the zero-order solution of the advancing front model
but include a mass transfer resistance in the continuous phase.
They showed that their results reduce to Ho's model when the mass
transfer resistance becomes negligible. Kim et al. include diffusion through a thin membrane film without droplets as an additional
resistance which is meant to simulate the observation that internal
water droplets cannot reach the surface of the emulsion globule.
This additional resistance is necessary because their technique of
volume-averaging the internal and membrane diffusion coefficients
underestimates the diffusive resistance for their conditions.

The advancing-front model of Ho et al. depends on two dimensionless parameters, ε and E. Physically, E is three times the original
mole ratio of internal reagent to bulk solute. For long times, if
$E/3$ is greater than 1, there is sufficient reagent to completely
remove the solute and no equilibrium is established. The second
dimensionless group, ε, measures the globule capacity for unreacted
solute relative to the reaction capacity provided by the reagent.
The value of ε is generally much less than 1. A notable feature of
the advancing-front theory is its algebraic solution permitting easy
calculation. One limitation of this approach is the assumption of
reaction irreversibility, which when combined with instantaneous
kinetics requires that the reagent concentration be identically zero
in the reacted region. This situation is asymptotically achieved
only for large equilibrium constant and large solute concentrations.

Teremoto and coworkers (94, 95) and Bunge and Noble (96) have
presented models which incorporate reaction equilibrium between solute and reagent throughout the globule. Their theories predict nonzero internal reagent concentration, and interdependent solute, reagent, and product concentrations within the globule. An additional
feature is that the differential equation locating the reaction
front becomes unnecessary since satisfying reaction equilibrium
turns the reaction on and off. One complicating feature of assuming
reversibility is that the apparent diffusion of solute through the
emulsion depends on the amount of solute reacted and hence varies
with local solute concentration within the membrane. Teremoto et
al. were forced to experimentally determine this enhanced effective
diffusivity. Bunge and Noble proposed a way to approximate this
effect using individual diffusion coefficients for the solute in the
internal and membrane phases, the initial concentration of reagent,
and the volume fraction of internal phase in the globule (96, 97).
Without any adjustable parameters, this reversible reaction model
predicts batch extraction data from measurable physical parameters:
diffusion coefficients, solute partition coefficients, and average
globule size.

Baird, et al. (97) recently presented further experimental evidence for the Bunge and Noble model using amine extraction with HCl.

They also extend the experimental data and model to include extraction from a solution of mixed solutes.
   The effect of size distribution in ELM systems has been studied.
Teremoto et al. (98) studied the effect of globule size distribution
on copper extraction. Their results indicated that the Sauter mean
diameter was sufficient to characterize the membrane size and it was
not necessary to use the size distribution. Hanna and Larson (99)
studied the influence of ELM preparation on the internal droplet
size distribution. They demonstrated the internal phase surface
area can affect extraction rate with a copper extraction system.
   Stelmaszek and coworkers have developed models for liquid membranes. Stelmaszek (100) modeled ELM droplets. Gladek et al. (101)
modeled ELMs in cocurrent and countercurrent flow processes. Gladek
et al. (82) used an advancing front approach to model ELM extraction.
   There have been some models developed for processes involving
ELMs. Wankat (102) and Wankat and Noble (103) developed analysis
procedures for three phase systems. This was done for both staged
and continuous contacting processes. Their results show that design
methods analogous to those for two phase systems can be used assuming that transport at one interface is limiting. Their design
methods include both analytical and graphical techniques.
   Hatton and coworkers have also analyzed processes involving
ELMs. Using their advancing-front model as a basis, they have
studied staged operations (104), continuous stirred tank reactors
(105), and mixer cascades (106). One interesting aspect of their
analysis is the effect of emulsion recycle. They analyzed the effect on extraction rate of recycling used emulsion and combining
this with new emulsion.
   Following the approach of Hatton, Reed and coworkers (107)
have analyzed continuous stirred tank extractors when reaction reversibility contributes. They have developed a simple way to extend
the simpler pseudo steady state advancing front model to predict
extractor performance even when reaction reversibility may be significant.

Overview

This volume is divided into three sections: theory, carrier
chemistry, and applications. The theory section includes chapters
which thoroughly describe the theory and analysis of various liquid
membrane types and configurations (107-110). The carrier chemistry
section contains two articles on the use of macrocycles for cation
separations (111-112). The applications section begins with a
survey article which thoroughly reviews the liquid membrane
applications in the literature and discusses both potential and
commercial aspects of liquid membrane technology. The remaining
articles discuss both gas phase (113-115) and liquid phase transport
(116-117).

Theory. The relationship of the chemical aspects of complexation reactions to the performance of facilitated transport membranes is discussed by Koval and Reyes (108). They describe a procedure which can be used to predict and optimize the facilitated transport of gases, including measurement of the appropriate equilibrium, transport, and kinetic parameters and structural modification of the carrier to improve the performance of the membrane. Examples of this procedure and carrier modification are given for derivatives of Fe(II) tetraimine complexes which reversibly bind CO in nitrile solvents (118). Experimental challenges in the measurement of the appropriate properties for other membrane configurations such as reactive ion exchange membranes and reactive polymer membranes are also discussed.

Stroeve and Kim (109) present a modeling study of parallel plate mass exchange devices with facilitated transport membranes. The separation is analyzed for the case of fully developed, one-dimensional, laminar flow of a Newtonian fluid in the mass exchange device. Parametric studies of the effects of the kinetic and transport properties are presented. The desirability of using facilitated transport membranes is found to depend on the mass transfer resistances in the membrane. When the membrane resistance is small, as in the case of many practical applications, the use of facilitated transport membranes is desirable to improve the separation performance of the device.

An approximate technique to model the performance of an hollow fiber ILM for the removal of HNO_3 by coupled transport is described by Noble and Danesi (110). The system was modeled as a series of ILM-continuous stirred tank reactor (CSTR) pairs. The approximate mathematical method used one adjustable parameter to predict steady-state nitric acid concentrations in good agreement with experimental data.

The next chapter is a modeling study of a continuous flow extraction system utilizing ELMs by Reed et al. (107). The authors consider the extraction of a solute which is trapped in the inner droplet phase by a chemical reaction. The paper compares predictions of the reversible reaction model of Bunge and Noble (96) to the advancing front model of Ho et al. (90) for a continuous flow ELM extractor. The calculational results show that assuming irreversible reaction can lead to underdesign of the process under conditions of high solute recovery where the outlet solute concentration is low. Under these conditions, an exact analytical solution to the reversible reaction model can be obtained.

Carrier Chemistry. The use of structurally modified macrocyclic polyethers (crown ethers) as carriers in bulk, emulsion, and immobilized liquid membranes is the subject of the chapter by Bartsch et al. (111). They discuss the use of ionizable crown ethers for the coupled transport of alkali metal cations. The ionizable carboxylic and phosphonic acid groups on the macrocycles eliminate the need for an anion to accompany the cation-macrocycle complex across the liquid membrane or for an auxillary complexing agent in the receiving phase. The influence of carrier structure on the selectivity and performance of competitive alkali metal transport across several kinds of liquid membranes is presented.

Izatt et al. (112) discuss the ELM extraction of metal ions
from aqueous source phases where the metal ion is present as a
complex anion or as a neutral complex using macrocyclic polyether
carriers. The parameters of co-anion type and metal ion
concentration are varied to tailor the selectivity of the separation.
Experimental data for the separation of Cd(II) from Zn(II) and/or
Hg(II), Au(I) from Ag(I), and Au(III) from Pd(II) or Ag(I) are given
to illustrate the application of this technique. The experimental
data are discussed in terms of various thermodynamic parameters.

Applications. This section begins with an extensive survey chapter.
Both potential and commercial applications are discussed.
    An alternative method for the preparation of facilitated
transport membranes is the subject of the first paper in this
section. Way and Noble (113) report a study of H_2S facilitated
transport in reactive ion exchange membranes. The use of a
perfluorosulfonic acid IEM as a support for organic amine
counterions avoids problems of solvent and carrier loss often
encountered with ILMs. High carrier loadings of greater than 8 M in
the IEMs were attained which helped to account for the high
facilitation factors of 26.4 which are observed at low H_2S partial
pressures. An analytical model predicted facilitation factors in
excellent agreement with the experimental data. Separation factors
for H_2S over CH_4 of 792 to 1200 are reported. Implications of the
mathematical model for industrial applications are also discussed.
    An alternative approach to solving stability problems with ILMs
is presented by Bhave and Sirkar (114). Aqueous solutions are
immobilized in the pore structure of hydophobic, polypropylene
hollow fibers by a solvent exchange procedure. Gas permeation
studies are reported at pressures up to 733 kPa with the high
pressure feed both on the shell and lumen sides of the laboratory
scale hollow fiber permeator. No deformation of the hollow fibers
is observed. Immobilizing a 30 weight % K_2CO_3 solution in the
hollow fibers greatly improved the separation factor, $\alpha(CO_2/N_2)$,
from 35.78 with pure water to 150.9 by a facilitated transport
mechanism. Performance comparisons with commercial CO_2 separation
membranes are made.
    Deetz (115) describes several experimental methods to overcome
the well known stability problems with ILMs for selective transport
of gases. He introduces methods to prepare ultra-thin (.1 to 2 μm)
stable, aqueous, immobilized liquid membranes. The problem of
volatilization of the liquid membrane can be reduced or eliminated
by immobilizing the liquid phase in pores small enough to
significantly reduce the molar free energy of the solution via the
Kelvin effect. Ultra-thin ILMs can be produced by selective
immobilization of the liquid membrane in the skin layer of a
microporous asymmetric polymer support.
    Watters et al. (116) describe a hybrid process known as
extractive ultrafiltration which combines ELM extraction and
ultrafiltration with the objective of removing trace levels of
organic contaminants from industrial waste water. Waste water
contacts the ELM and the organic solutes are extracted. The
emulsion is recovered from the stream via ultrafiltration. The
ultrafilter permeate is purified water while the retentate emulsion

phase is recycled. The feasibility of the process is demonstrated
using toluene as a model organic contaminant.

Muscatello et al. (117) discuss the use of hollow fiber ILMs
containing bifunctional organophosphorus extractants to remove
americium and plutonium from nitrate-nitric acid waste streams. A
reduction in the actinide concentration in a waste stream would
allow disposal of the stream as a low-level waste. Partial
neutralization of the nitric acid in the waste stream was necessary
to obtain high (>94%) removal of the Am(III).

Summary

This overview chapter has the objective of introducing the Symposium
Series volume and the subject of liquid membrane technology. If
membranes are viewed as semi-permeable phase separators, then the
traditional concept of membranes as polymer films can be extended to
include liquids and liquid-swollen polymers. The addition of a
mobile complexation agent to the membrane is known as facilitated
liquid membrane separation. Often, in liquid phase facilitated
transport systems, the solute flux is coupled to the opposite flux
of another species. This process, common in metal ion recovery
schemes, is known as coupled transport.

Liquid membranes can be prepared in several configurations.
Emulsifying the receiving liquid phase in an immiscible liquid membrane
phase and stabilizing the dispersion with a surfactant is known as
a liquid surfactant (110) or emulsion liquid membrane. An immobilized
liquid membrane is prepared by impregnating the pore structure of a
microporous polymer film with the liquid membrane, which may contain
a complexation agent. Depending on the support, immobilized liquid
membranes are fabricated in flat sheet or hollow fiber configurations.

The tutorial section of this chapter also discusses typical
experimental techniques and a survey of theoretical approaches. The
authors' papers encompass the entire breadth of the technology and are
presented with the intention of furthering research and industrial
applications of liquid membranes.

Literature Cited

1.   Noble, R.D. Sep. Sci. Tech. 1987, 22(243), 731-743.
2.   Lonsdale, H.K. J. Mem. Sci. 1982, 10, 81-181.
3.   Way, J.D., Noble, R.D., and Batemen, B.R. (1985). Selection of
     Supports for Immobilized Liquid Membranes. In Material Science
     of Synthetic Membranes. ACS Symposium Series No. 269, D.L.
     Lloyd, editor.
4.   LeBlanc, O.G.; Ward, W.J.; Matson, S.L.; Kimura, S.G. J. Mem.
     Sci. 1980, 6, 339.
5.   Hsu, E.C., Li, N.N., and Hucal, T. (1983). U.S. Patent
     4,419,200.
6.   King, C.J. (1983). Separation Processes Based on Reversible
     Chemical Complexation. Proceedings of Joint Conference on Sepa-
     ration Processes, Taipei, Taiwan.
7.   Goddard, J.D. J. Phys. Chem. 1985, 89, 1825-1830.
8.   Dehmlow, E.V. and Dehmlow, S S. Phase Transfer Catalysis, 2nd
     Edition. Verlag-Chemie Pub. Co. Monographs in Modern Chemistry
     1983; Vol. 11.

9. Fendler, J.H. "Membrane Mimetic Chemistry," John Wiley: New York, 1982.
10. Hanna, G.J. and Noble, R.D. Chem. Rev. 1985, 85, 583-598.
11. Schultz, J.S., Goddard, J.D., and Suchdeo, S.R. A.I.Ch.E. J. 1974, 20(3), 417-444.
12. Goddard, J.D., Schultz, J.S., and Suchdeo, S.R. A.I.Ch.E. J. 1974, 20(4), 625-645.
13. Cussler, E.L. and Evans, D.F. Sep. Pur. Meth. 1974, 3, 399.
14. Smith, D.R.; Lander, R.J.; Quinn, J.A. In Recent Developments in Separation Science; N.N. Li, Ed.; CRC Press: Cleveland, OH, 1977; Vol. 3, p 225.
15. Godddard, J.D. Chem. Eng. Sci. 1977, 32, 795-809.
16. Kimura, S.G.; Matson, S.L.; Ward, W.J. III. In Recent Developments in Separation Science; Li, N.N., Ed.; CRC Press: Cleveland, OH, 1979; Vol. 5, p 11.
17. Halwachs, W. and Schugerl, R. Int. Chem. Eng. 1980, 20, 519.
18. Way, J.D., Noble, R.D., Flynn, T.M., and Sloan, E.D. J. Mem. Sci. 1982, 12, 239-259.
19. Meldon, J.H., Stroeve, P., and Gregoire, C.K. Chem. Eng. Comm. 1982, 16, 263.
20. Marr, R. and Kopp, A. Int. Chem. Eng. 1982, 22, 44.
21. Matson, S.L., Lopez, J., and Quinn, J.A. Chem. Eng. Sci. 1983, 38(4), 503-524.
22. Danesi, P.R. Sep. Sci. Tech. 1984a, 11&12, 857-894.
23. Noble, R.D.; Way, J.D.; Bunge, A.L. In Solvent Extraction and Ion Exchange; Morinsky, J.A. and Marcus, Y., Ed.; Marcel Dekker: New York, 1987; Vol. 10, in press.
24. Ward, W.J. III. A.I.Ch.E. J. 1970a, 16, 405-410.
25. Ward, W.J. III and Robb, W.L. Science 1967, 156, 1481-1484.
26. Ward, W.J. III. Nature 1970b, 227, 162-163.
27. Otto, N.C. and Quinn, J.A. Chem. Eng. Sci. 1971, 26, 949-961.
28. Rose, G.D. and Quinn, J.A. J. Col. Inter. Sci. 1968, 27, 193.
29. Suchdeo, S.R. and Schultz, J.S. Chem. Eng. Sci. 1974, 29, 13-23.
30. Matson, S.L., Herrick, C.S., and Ward, W.J. III I&EC Proc. Des. Dev. 1977, 16, 370.
31. Baker, R.W., Tuttle, M.E., Kelly, D.J., and Lonsdale, H.K. J. Mem. Sci. 1977, 2, 213.
32. Babcock, W.C., Baker, R.W., LaChapelle, E.D., and Smith, K.L. J. Mem. Sci. 1980a, 7, 71-87.
33. Babcock, W.C., Baker, R.W., LaChapelle, E.D., and Smith, K.L. J. Mem. Sci. 1980b, 7, 89-100.
34. Bateman, B.R, Way, J.D., and Larson, K.M. Sep. Sci. Tech. 1984, 19(1), 21-32.
35. Smith, D.R. and Quinn, J.A. A.I.Ch.E. J. 1980, 26, 112.
36. Hughes, R.D.; Mahoney, J.A.; Steigelmann, E.F. In Recent Development In Separation Science; Li, N.N.; Caol, J.M., Eds.; CRC Press: Cleveland, OH, 1986; Vol. 9, p 173.
37. Way, J.D., Noble, R.D.; Reed, D.L.; Ginley, G.M.; Jarr, L.A. AIChE J., 1987, 33(3), 480-487.
38. Donaldson, T.L. and Quinn, J.A. Chem. Eng. Sci. 1975, 30, 103.
39. Adamson, A.W. Physical Chemistry of Surfaces; John Wiley: New York, 1976.
40. Kopp, A.G. Ph.D. Thesis, Technical University of Graz, Austria, 1978.

41. Frankenfeld, J.W., Cahn, R.P., and Li, N.N. Sep. Sci. Tech.
     1981, 16, 385-402.
42. Kemena, L.L., Noble, R.D., and Kemp, N.J. J. Mem. Sci. 1983,
     15, 259-274.
43. Olander, D.R. A.I.Ch.E. J. 1960, 6, 233-2239.
44. Friedlander S.K. and Keller, K.H. Chem. Eng. Sci. 1965, 20,
     121-129.
45. Secor, R.M. and Beutler, J.A. A.I.Ch.E. J. 1967, 13, 365-373.
46. Hoofd, L. and Kreuzer, F. J. Math. Biol. 1979, 8, 1-13.
47. Hoofd, L. and Kreuzer, F. A.I.Ch.E. Symposium Series 1981,
     77(202), 123-129.
48. Noble, R.D.; Way, J.D.; Powers, L.A. I&EC Fund. 1986, 25, 450.
49. Cussler, E.L., Evans, D.F., and Matesich, M.A. Science 1971,
     172, 377-379.
50. Noble, R.D. Sep. Sci. Tech. 1984, 19(8&9), 469-478.
51. Teremoto, M. and Tarrimoto, H. Sep. Sci. Tech. 1983c, 18,
     871-892.
52. Goddard, J.D., Schultz, J.S., and Bassett, R.J. Chem. Eng.
     Sci. 1970, 25, 665-683.
53. Kreuzer, F. and Hoofd, L. Resp. Phys. 1972, 15, 104-124.
54. Smith, D.R. and Quinnn, J.A. A.I.Ch.E. J. 1979, 25, 197-200.
55. Suchdeo, S.R. and Schultz, J.S. A.I.Ch.E. Chemical Engineering
     Progress Symposium Series "Advances in Bioengineering" 1971,
     67(114), 165-173.
56. Yung, D. and Probstein, R.F. J. Phys. Chem. 1973, 77,
     2201-2205.
57. Jain, R. and Schultz, J.S. J. Mem. Sci. 1982, 11(1), 79-106.
58. Folkner, C.A. and Noble, R.D. J. Mem. Sci. 1983, 12, 289-301.
59. Niiya, K.Y. and Noble, R.D. J. Mem. Sci. 1985, 23(2), 183-198.
60. Way, J.D., Ph.D. Thesis, University of Colorado, Boulder, 1986.
61. Noble, R.D. Sep. Sci. Tech. 1985, 20, 577-585.
62. Spaan, J.A.E. Pflugers Arch. 1973, 342, 289-306.
63. Curl, R.L. and Schultz, J.S. Adv. Exp. Med. Biol. 1973, 37B,
     929-935.
64. Spaan, J.A.E., Kreuzer, F., and Hoofd, L. Pflugers Arch. 1980,
     384, 231-239.
65. Kemp, N.J. and Noble, R.D. Sep. Sci. Tech. 1984, 18,
     1147-1165.
66. Ruchkenstein, E. and Sasidhar, V. J. Mem. Sci. 1982, 12,
     27-50.
67. Leiber, J.P., Noble, R.D., Way, J.D., and Bateman, B.R. Sep.
     Sci. Tech. 1985, 20(4), 231-256.
68. Athayde, A.L. and Ivory, C.F. J. Mem. Sci. 1985, 23, 241-256.
69. Goddard, J.D. A.I.Ch.E. Symposium Series 1981, 77(202),
     114-122.
70. Shimidzu, T. and Yoshikawa, M. J. Mem. Sci. 1983, 13, 1-13.
71. Jain, R. and Schultz, J.S. J. Mem. Sci. 1983, 15, 63-80.
72. Stroeve, P., Smith, K.A., and Colton, C.K. A.I.Ch.E. J. 1976,
     22, 1125-1132.
73. Stroeve, P. and Eagle, K. Chem. Eng. Comm. 1979, 3, 189-198.
74. Danesi, P.R., Horwitz, E.P., Vandegrift, G.F., and Chiarizia,
     R. Sep. Sci. Tech. 1981, 16, 201.
75. Danesi, P.R. J. Mem. Sci. 1984b, 20, 231-248.
76. Danesi, P.R.; Reichley-Yinger, L. J. Mem. Sci. 1986, 29,
77. Chan, C.C. and Lee, C.J. J. Mem. Sci. 1984, 20, 1-24.

78. Kremesec, V.J. Sep. Purif. Meth. 1981, 10, 117.
79. Kremesec, V.J. and Slattery, J.C. A.I.Ch.E. J. 1982, 28, 492.
80. Cahn, R.P. and Li, N.N. Sep. Sci. 1974, 9, 505.
81. Boyadzhiev. L., Sapundzhiev, T., and Bezenshek, E. Sep. Sci. 1978, 12, 541.
82. Gladek, L., Stelmaszek, J., and Szust, J. J. Mem. Sci. 1982, 12, 153-167.
83. Matulevicius, E.S. and Li, N.N. Sep. Purif. Meth. 1975, 4, 73.
84. Hochhauser, A.M. and Cussler, E.L. A.I.Ch.E. Symp. Ser. 1975, 71(152), 136-142.
85. Way, J.D. and Noble, R.D. A Macroscopic Model of a Continous Emulision Liquid Membrane Extraction System. In Residence Time Distribution Theory in Chemical Engineering. Verlag-Chemie Pub. Co. A. Petho and R.D. Noble, editors. 1982; pp. 247-254.
86. Teremoto, M., Sakai, T., Yanagawa, K., and Miyake, Y. Sep. Sci. Tech. 1983d, 18, 985-997.
87. Noble, R.D. I&EC Fund. 1983, 22(1), 139-144.
88. Stroeve, P., Varanasi, P.P., and Hoofd, L.J.C. J.Mem. Sci. 1984, 19, 155-172.
89. Kopp, A.G., Marr, R.J., and Moser, F.E. Inst. Chem. Eng. Symp. Ser. 1978, 54, 279-290.
90. Ho, W.S., Hatton, T.A., Lightfoot, E.N., and Li, N.N. A.I.Ch.E. J. 1982, 28, 662-670.
91. Kim, K., Choi, S., and Ihm, S. I&EC Fund. 1983, 22, 167.
92. Fales, J.L. and Stroeve, P. J. Mem. Sci. 1984, 21, 35-54.
93. Stroeve, P. and Varanasi, P.P. A.I.Ch.E. J. 1984, 30, 1007-1009.
94. Teremoto, M., Takihana, H., Shibutani, M., Yuasa, T., Miyake, Y., and Teranishi, H. J. Chem. Eng. Japan 1981, 14, 122.
95. Teremoto, M., Takihana, H., Shibutani, M., Yussa, T., and Hara, N. Sep. Sci. Tech. 1983a, 18, 397-420.
96. Bunge, A.L. and Noble, R.D. J. Mem. Sci. 1984, 21, 55-71.
97. Baird, R.S., Bunge, A.L., Noble, R.D. A.I.Ch.E. J. 1987, 33, 43-53.
98. Teremoto, M., Sakai, T., Yanagawa, K., Ohsuga, M., and Miyake, Y. Sep. Sci. Tech. 1983b, 18, 735-764.
99. Hanna, G.J. and Larson, K.M. I&EC Prod. Res. Dev. 1985, 24(2), 269-274.
100. Stelmaszek, J. In Recent Developments in Separation Science; Li, N.N., Ed.; CRC Press: Cleveland, OH, 1981; Vol. 6, p 11.
101. Gladek, L., Stelmaszek, J., and Szust, J. Rec. Dev. Sep. Sci. 1981, VI: 29-49.
102. Wankat, P.C. I&EC Fund. 1980, 19, 358-363.
103. Wankat, P.C. and Noble, R.D. I&EC Fund. 1984, 23, 137-143.
104. Hatton, T.A. and Wardius, D.S. A.I.Ch.E. J. 1984, 30, 934.
105. Hatton, T.A., Lightfoot, E.N., Cahn, R.P., and Li, N.N. I&CE Fund. 1983, 22, 27-35.
106. Wardius, D.S. and Hatton, T.A. Chem. Eng. Comm. 1985, 37, 159-171.
107. Reed, D.L.; Bunge. A.L.; Noble, R.D. In Liquid Membranes: Theory and Applications; Noble, R.D., Way, J.D., Eds. American Chemical Society: Washington, D.C., 1987.
108. Koval, C.A.; Reyes, Z.E. ibidem.
109. Stroeve, P.; Kim, J. ibidem.
110. Noble, R.D.; Danesi, P.R. ibidem.

111. Bartsch, R.A.; Charewicz, W.A.; Kang, S.I.; Walkowiak, W.
     ibidem.
112. Izatt, R.M.; Bruening, R.L.; Christensen, J.J. ibidem.
113. Way, J.D. and Noble, R.D. ibidem.
114. Bhave, R.R.; Sirkar, K.K. ibidem.
115. Deetz, D.W. ibidem.
116. Watters, J.C.; Murrer, D.G.; Fleischman, M.; Klein, E. ibidem.
117. Muscatello, A.C.; Navratil, J.D.; Price, M.Y. ibidem.
118. Koval, C.A, Noble, R.D., Way, J.D., Louie, B., Reyes, A., Horn,
     G. and Reed, D. Inorgan. Chem. 1985, 24, 1147-1152.
119. Li, N.N. 1968, U.S. Patent 3410 794.

RECEIVED May 11, 1987

THEORY

Chapter 2

Chemical Aspects of Facilitated Transport Through Liquid Membranes

Carl A. Koval and Zelideth E. Reyes

Department of Chemistry and Biochemistry, University of Colorado, Boulder, CO 80309

Reversible complexation reactions can be utilized to facilitate the transport of molecules from the gas phase across liquid membranes resulting in a selective separation. The effectiveness of the transport can be related to key physical properties of the system. Results for several systems are compared to the predictions of mathematical models. Advantages and difficulties associated with the use of ion-exchange membranes are discussed. Several areas for future research are suggested.

Facilitated transport (FT) through liquid membranes is a phenomenon that allows the flux of a particular molecule in the gas phase (permeate) through the membrane to be enhanced. This enhanced flux is due to a reversible reaction between the permeate and a chemical carrier, which has been incorporated in the membrane, to form a carrier-permeate complex. In contrast with separations based on retention chromatography, FT requires mobility of the complex so that it can diffuse in response to the permeate concentration gradient across the membrane.

The study of FT phenomena has widespread relevance to areas other than gas separations. The complexation chemistry itself can be applied to analytical techniques such as liquid-liquid extraction and chromatography (1) or to industrial separations such as extractive and azeotropic distillations and stripping processes (2). Transport studies utilizing synthetic membranes are important for understanding biological membrane processes (3). There are potential applications based on FT for in vivo drug delivery and maintenance of self-contained environments. FT through liquid membranes is particularly attractive for industrial separations because the energy requirements are low yet it is possible to achieve high fluxes and selectivity (4). FT membrane systems have already been used in the treatment of heavy metals, such as chromium in hydrometallurgical ore processing, and in the extraction of oxygen from air (5).

0097-6156/87/0347-0028$06.00/0

Our objective has been to develop a procedure through which fundamental properties of reversible complexation reaction systems can be used to predict and to optimize FT of gases. This procedure includes the selection of carriers, the measurement of the relevant physical properties (RPP) and fluxes, the use of an optimization model to identify factors that limit the transport, and the modification of the carrier to improve the facilitation.

Mathematical Model

The complexation and diffusion processes involved in FT are shown in Figure 1. The physical constants of the system that are relevant to FT are the complexation equilibrium and rate constants, K(eq), k(f) and k(r), the diffusion coefficients for the permeate and complex, D(A) and D(AC), initial concentrations of all species in the membrane solution phase, and the membrane thickness (L). The interplay of these parameters in determining the flux of permeate through the membrane is a complicated transport problem.

Several mathematical models that attempt to describe FT have been reported (4). One such model developed by Noble and coworkers (6,7) combines the physical constants mentioned above into three dimensionless parameters:

$$\mathbf{K} = K(eq)[A] \tag{1}$$

$$\boldsymbol{\epsilon} = D(AC)/k(r)L^2 \tag{2}$$

$$\boldsymbol{\alpha} = \{D(AC)/D(A)\}\{([C]+[AC])/[A]\} \tag{3}$$

The parameters $\mathbf{K}$, $\boldsymbol{\epsilon}$ and $\boldsymbol{\alpha}$ can be used to calculate a facilitation factor, $\mathbf{F}$, which is defined as:

$$\mathbf{F} = \frac{\text{flux with carrier in the membrane}}{\text{flux with no carrier in the membrane}} \tag{4}$$

The equilibrium factor $\mathbf{K}$ is a measure of the magnitude of complexation at a given permeate concentration. The inverse kinetic factor $\boldsymbol{\epsilon}$ is the ratio of reaction time to diffusion time. A small value of $\boldsymbol{\epsilon}$ corresponds to a diffusion-limited transport, while a large $\boldsymbol{\epsilon}$ corresponds to a kinetically-limited transport. The concentration/mobility factor, $\boldsymbol{\alpha}$, compares the concentration and diffusion coefficient of the complex to that of the permeate.

For values of $\mathbf{K}$, $\boldsymbol{\epsilon}$ and $\boldsymbol{\alpha}$ that are likely to be achieved in real membrane systems, F ranges from unity, which implies no facilitation, to values greater than twenty! In reference 7, a series of working curves were presented that depict the relationships between these four parameters and predict optimal values of $\mathbf{K}$, $\boldsymbol{\epsilon}$ and $\boldsymbol{\alpha}$, i.e. values which yield the highest values of $\mathbf{F}$. One interesting feature of predictions in reference 7 is that F reaches optimal values for $\mathbf{K}$= 1-100. Large values of $\mathbf{F}$ require a compromise between uptake of permeate at the feed side and the release of permeate at the sweep side of the membrane. For K > 100, the concentration of free permeate in the membrane becomes small which inhibits the release of permeate at the sweep

side of the membrane. For $K < 1$, complexation of the permeate
becomes unimportant, since there is not a significant concentration
of the complex with respect to that of unbound permeate in the
membrane. In general, the magnitude of F is inversely related to
the kinetic factor ε. Inspection of Equation 2 reveals that small
values of ε are most easily achieved by large values of L or k(r)
which lead to more time for the complexation reaction. Finally, F
always increases with increasing values of the
concentration/mobility factor α.

Metal Ions and Complexes as Carriers

In 1960, Scholander described an eight-fold increase in the steady
state flux of O_2 through aqueous solutions containing hemoglobin
(8). Since that time, metal ions have been shown to provide FT in
a number of systems: Cu(I) as a carrier for CO (9-11), Fe(II) as
a carrier for NO (12-14), and Ag(I) as a carrier for olefins
(3,15).
         It should be possible to improve the utility of metal ions as
carriers via the formation of complex ions. Complex ions derived
from macrocycles or other polydentate are especially attractive for
studying FT. Macrocyclic complexes are relatively stable. Since the
ligand occupies most of the coordination sites on the metal ion, FT
based on 1:1 reaction between the complex and the metal can be
studied within the context of simple mathematical models.
Furthermore, macrocycles have been utilized to study the effects of
ring size, degree of saturation, overall charge, ligand
conformation, ligand field ,and π-bonding on the coordination
chemistry of metal ions (16). Thus, the binding of permeates by
macrocyclic complex carriers can be varied in a systematic way
allowing for optimization of a membrane system.
         In an attempt to illustrate the concepts described above, we
have studied the reversible binding of carbon monoxide by several
Fe(II) tetraimine complexes in benzonitrile. The Fe(II) complex
derived from the macrocyclic ligand 2,3,9,10-tetramethyl-1,4,8,11-
tetraaza-cyclotetradeca-1,3,8,10-tetraene (TIM) was first prepared
by Baldwin et al. (17). They demonstrated that the nitrile
solvent ligands could be replaced by other ligands such as
imidazole and CO. Carbon monoxide replaces only one of the axial
nitrile ligands at ambient presssures, as illustrated in Figure 2
(for Fe(TIM), $R_1 = R_2 = CH_3$ and $R_3 = H$). Due to a relatively
positive Fe(III,II) reduction potential, Fe(TIM) is stable in
oxygen-saturated benzonitrile (BN) solutions for weeks and in the
solid state for months. The stability of this complex towards
oxidation in benzonitrile together with the known 1:1 complexation
reaction with CO suggested the possibility of constructing a
membrane system for the separation of CO from O_2.
         By following electronic spectral changes of Fe(TIM) in BN upon
reaction with CO as a function of time the rates and equilibrium
constants for the complexation reaction were determined (18). The
diffusion coefficients for the carrier and the CO-complex as well
as the equilibrium constant were measured using cyclic voltammetry
and rotating disk voltammetry. These physical constants were
incorporated in the optimization model which predicted a
facilitation factor F= 1.12. This data is summarized in Table I.
The fluxes of O_2 and CO through a membrane of filter paper

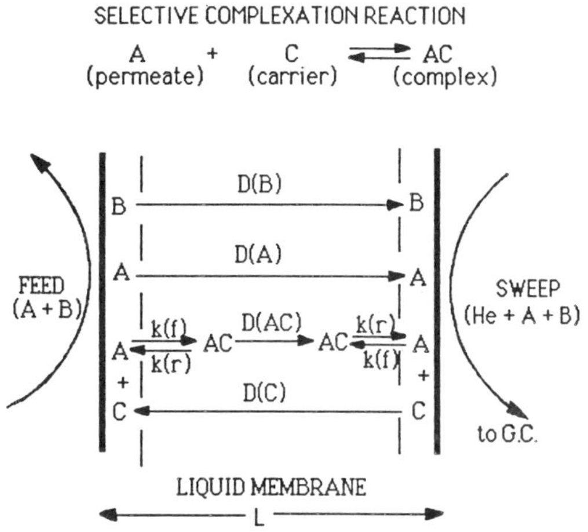

SELECTIVE COMPLEXATION REACTION

$$A \quad + \quad C \quad \rightleftharpoons \quad AC$$
(permeate)   (carrier)   (complex)

Figure 1. Cross-sectional view of processes in a liquid membrane that result in facilitated transport of species A. The flux of species B is solely due to diffusion.

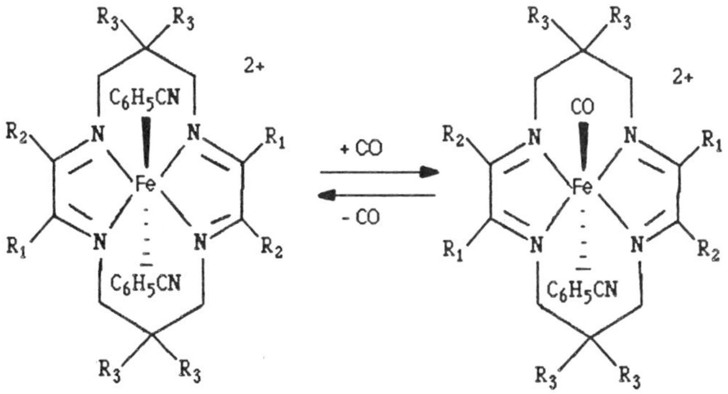

Figure 2. Structural drawing depicting the reversible 1:1 complexation reaction of Fe(II) macrocyclic complex ions with carbon monoxide.

impregnated with Fe(TIM)/BN were measured utilizing a flow cell and
gas chromatography (19). The experimental $F= 1.14 \pm .09$
compared favorably with the predicted value. Despite the small F
that was obtained, the excellent agreement between the experimental
results and the model encouraged the use of the optimization model
to determine which properties of the system were limiting the FT.
Although substitution kinetics for the low-spin Fe(II) center are
relatively slow, the limiting factor was α, i.e. the solubility of
the carrier.

Recently, we have attempted to increase F for this system by
investigating derivatives of Fe(TIM) (20). These derivatives are:
Fe(Me$_4$TIM) with $R_1 = R_2 = R_3 = CH_3$ and Fe(Me$_2$Ph$_2$TIM) with $R_1 = CH_3$,
$R_2 = C_6H_5$ and $R_3 = H$. As shown in Table I, these Fe(TIM) analogs
are more soluble in benzonitrile. Unfortunately the complexation
equilibrium constants are smaller for the derivatives, which
results in poorer values of K under the conditions of the
transport experiments. The complexation kinetics for Fe(Me$_4$TIM) are
considerably faster than those observed for Fe(TIM). The value of
k(r) for Fe(Me$_2$Ph$_2$TIM) is also greater than the value for Fe(TIM)
while the value of k(f) is about the same. The diffusion
coefficients for all three carriers are about the same as expected.
Based on the values of K, ϵ and α that can be calculated from
the RPP in Table I, Fe(Me$_4$TIM) should be a much better carrier than
Fe(TIM); however, results of transport experiments showed only a
slight increase in F. We believe that this discrepancy is due to
the value of D(AC) used in the calculations. The values of D(AC)
reported in Table I were measured at concentrations ranging from
2–5 mM, which are much smaller than those used in the transport
experiments. Recently, we have found that lower values of D(AC) are
obtained at higher concentrations, presumably due to the formation
of dimers or oligomers. Based on the RPP's, Fe(Me$_2$Ph$_2$TIM) should be
a comparable carrier to Fe(TIM) yet the value of F observed is
much larger. It is possible that the value of F(obsd) is erroneous
due to a leak in the membrane and we are attempting to repeat this
experiment.

Table I. Summary of Physical Properties and Facilitation Factors
for Fe(II)(TIM) and Derivatives

Carrier	Solubility	K(eq)	k(f)	k(r)	D(AC)	F_{calc}	F_{obsd}
	(mM)	(M^{-1})	$(M^{-1}s^{-1})$	(s^{-1})	$(cm^2 s^{-1})$		
Fe(TIM)	15	420	0.14	3.3×10^{-4}	3.1×10^{-6}	1.12	1.14
Fe(Me$_4$TIM)	46	180	0.92	5.0×10^{-3}	2.5×10^{-6}	1.86	1.23
Fe(Me$_2$Ph$_2$TIM)	50	130	0.11	9.0×10^{-4}	4.8×10^{-6}	1.28	2.8

In addition to carrier derivatization, we attempted to
increase the solubility of the Fe(II) carriers through the addition
of co-solvents to the liquid membrane. Addition of 50% (v:v)
propylene carbonate to benzonitrile resulted in six- to eightfold
increase in solubility without loss of stability towards dioxygen.

Unfortunately, the reaction of the Fe(II)(TIM) complex with CO becomes complicated in the mixed solvent. The reaction displays pseudo-first-order behavior only at long times (>200 s) and cyclic voltammetry reveals more than one electroactive component, even in the absence of CO. It is possible that propylene carbonate displaces benzonitrile as an axial ligand to Fe(II) and that this substitution results in the formation of a high-spin complex.

General Properties of Immobilized Liquid Membranes, Ion-Exchange
Membranes and Polymeric Membranes

Despite the physical strength offered by a macroporous support, most immobilized liquid membrane (ILM) systems are not practical for industrial separations because they are not sufficiently stable. The two most important types of instability are solvent evaporation and loss of solvent and/or carrier from the support caused by a pressure differential across the membrane. These instabilities can be completely eliminated by removing the solvent, i.e., replacing the liquid membrane with a polymeric membrane (PM).

Polymeric membranes have been of interest for industrial separations for some time. The main advantage of PM's with respect to ILM's is stability. The main disadvantages of PM's are low solubility of the permeate and lack of selectivity. Carriers can be introduced into a PM either via co-polymerization of appropriate monomers or by chemically bonding the carrier to appropriate functional groups on the polymer backbone. Recently, there have been two reports of facilitated dioxygen transport utilizing this approach (21,22). In each case, a transition metal complex in which the metal is known to bind dioxygen was introduced into the a PM. Even though enhanced oxygen fluxes were reported, these results cannot be explained using the framework of facilitated transport as defined earlier in this paper. Facilitation in ILM's required that the carrier and complex can diffuse freely within the membrane. In the limit of zero mobility of the carrier and complex, which is presumably the case for a PM, the membrane material should retard the permeate as is the case for numerous polymeric materials currently used as chromatographic supports. This effect is illustrated by the recent report of a material prepared by the immobilization of Co(II) Schiff-base complexes on a polystyrene/polypyridine copolymer (1).

Ion-exchange membranes (IEM's) are polymeric materials that contain ionic functionalities chemically bound to the polymer backbone. The bound ionic functionalities can be anionic or cationic. In order to maintain electroneutrality within the membrane, each bound ionic site must be paired with an ion of the opposite charge. When the membrane is swollen with an appropriate solvent, these ions become mobile and can be exchanged with other ions of like charge. The internal structure of certain IEM's such as Nafion (23) results in a property known as permselectivity. Permselective IEM's reject ions of the same charge as the bound ionic sites, i.e. in Nafion vitually all the ionic conductivity through the membrane is due to the mobile cations.

With respect to FT, IEM's that have been swollen with solvent display properties that are intermediate between ILM's and PM's. Carriers that have the same charge as the mobile ions can be exchanged into the IEM simply by soaking the IEM in a solution

containing the carrier in an ionic form. It is often possible to
exchange more than 90% of the mobile ions which leads to very high
carrier concentrations (1 - 10 M). High concentrations of carrier
are necessary for large values of the dimensionless parameter α
and large facilitation factors. In general, IEM's are far more
stable than ILM's, at least on the timescale of flux measurements
(2-12 h). Since the solvent interacts with the support material, it
evaporates much more slowly. The pores in IEM's such as Nafion are
relatively narrow (<10 nm) and the membranes can withstand moderate
pressure differentials.

The major disadvantage of IEM's with respect to ILM's is that
the carriers and complex will be less mobile in the IEM. As noted
by Elliott and Redepenning (24), diffusion coefficients for ions
in non-viscous solvents vary by little more than an order of
magnitude, 10(E-06) - 10(E-05) cm(E+02)/s. In Nafion, diffusion
coefficients for cations ranging from 10(E-12) to 10(E-06)
cm(E+02)/s have been reported (24). Clearly, if the diffusion
coefficient for a complex is at the lower end of this range
facilitated transport will be almost nil because the diffusion time
will be long resulting in an undesirable value of ε.

Difficulties Associated with the Measurement of Relevant Physical
Properties in Ion-Exchange Membranes

Since IEM's offer greater stability than ILM's and greater
selectivity and permeability than PM's, it would be useful to be
able to model transport processes in these materials and to predict
the effectiveness of facilitated transport based on relevant
physical properties (RPP). Although it may be necessary to modify
the model developed for ILM's in order to completely describe
transport processes in IEM's, it is likely that most of the same
RPP's of the system will be important. The purpose of this section
is to point out that measurement of RPP's in IEM's, especially
permselective IEM's, may be difficult. Although problems with model
development and property measurement exist, carrier impregnated
IEM's can produce rapid and selective separations of gas mixtures.
Way and co-workers have incorporated the monoprotonated
ethylenediamine cation into Nafion membranes to achieve the
separation of carbon dioxide from methane (25).

Experimentally, there are two distinct methods for measuring
diffusion coefficients in IEM's. If the mobile ions are
electroactive, the IEM can be positioned on the surface of an
electrode. By applying an appropriate potential to the electrode,
the redox state of the mobile ion is changed resulting in a
concentration gradient within the membrane. The current response
can be used to calculate D (24,26). Those who wish to use this
method are encouraged to read the paper by Elliott and Redepenning.
These authors illustrate that different electrochemical methods
yield widely discrepant values of D and suggest reasons for these
discrepancies. A straightforward albeit tedious method for
measuring D in IEM's involves isotopic labeling of mobile ions and
their subsequent diffusion between compartments of a cell separated
by the IEM (27).

Coupling of ion mobilities within permselective IEM's (28)
complicates the measurement of diffusion coefficients within these
membranes. These determinations are unambiguous only when a single

mobile ion is present in the IEM and the solution surrounding it. Due to these complications and to the limited number of FT experiments that have been performed with IEM's, it is not yet possible to ascertain which method for measuring values of D allow prediction of the flux or the facilitation factor.

The second difficulty associated with measurement of properties relevant to facilitated transport across IEM's is the complexation chemistry itself. Since the support materials in ILM's do not interact with the permeate, carrier or complex, the thermodynamic and kinetic constants for the complexation reaction can be measured in pure solvent. Using these same constants to predict transport across IEM's will almost certainly result in significant errors. If the complexation reaction involves the formation of ions, the value of K(eq) will be different in the IEM due to the different activites of the ions.

A change in the equilibrium constant requires changes in the forward or reverse rate constants as well. Recently, Lewis compared rate and activation parameters for complexation reactions within Nafion with those in solution (29). Lewis measured the rate constants for the reaction,

$$Ru(II)(NH_3)_5(H_2O)^{2+} + py\text{-}R \longrightarrow Ru(II)(NH_3)_5(py\text{-}R)^{2+}$$

where py-R represents a series of substituted pyridines. The rate and activation parameters were significantly different from values reported for the same reactions in water.

It is also conceivable that complexation reactions in IEM's could have completely different products and mechanisms than the reaction between the carrier and permeate in pure solvent. Clearly, the answer to these questions lies in developing experimental methods for the in-situ determination of the structure of the complex and the values of RPP's in IEM's.

Possible Areas for Future Research
Increased use of liquid membranes for practical purposes will require additional research. One area that will clearly require the input of chemists is the synthesis of selective and stable carriers. The general characteristics of an effective carrier can be delineated from the material presented in the Introduction section. The carrier must have a high solubility (>0.1 M) in the liquid membrane, be stable in solution as the carrier and complex. and react reversibly and selectively with the permeate. The optimal value of the chemical equilibrium constant K(eq) depends on the concentration of the permeate in the membrane, but the value of the dimensionless equilibrium constant **K** should be close to 10. The kinetics of the complexation reaction should be fast compared to the time it takes the permeate and complex to diffuse across the membrane. The selectivity of the separation will depend on the lack of reactivity of the carrier with other componenets of the matrix that contains the permeate. With these constraints in mind, chemists can begin to search for carriers with desirable complexation selectivities and to develop structure/property relationships that would lead to the design of carriers with optimal RPP's.

At this point in time, an increased awareness on the part of

chemists as to the separation problems that are important in the
private sector would be extremely useful. This information could be
provided by the industrial and chemical engineering communities.
One example of a pertinant problem is the need for carriers for
dioxygen that are not susecptible to autoxidation.

This paper has stressed the ability to predict the
effectiveness of facilitated transport based on measurable physical
properties of the system (RPP). Understanding which properties
limit the transport is essential for improving separations in a
systematic way. Although the agreement between mathematical models
and experimental data is acceptable for ILM's involving simple
complexation reactions, this methodology should be extended to more
complex systems. Some of the areas requiring additional attention
include:

Extension of mathematical models to include more complicated
complexation chemistry. In particular, carriers with more than one
binding site might be more effective than 1:1 binders. It should be
noted that extremely large carriers, such as proteins, may suffer
from low mobility and/or low solubility.

Development of additional experimental procedures for measuring
transport rates. Most of the instrumental designs available are
elaborate and/or expensive. Transport of permeates contained within
liquid phases as well as in the gas phase must be considered.

Development of membrane support materials that provide greater
stability than ILM's but still allow the systematic incorporation
of carriers. Far greater understanding of diffusional processes
and chemical reactions within IEM's is essential. The necessity for
in situ experimental techniques was discussed in the previous
section.

Understanding of solubilities and transport phenomena within
polymeric membranes containing immobilized carriers. It in unclear
why these materials lead to retention of permeates in some
instances and enhanced fluxes in others.

Finally, an exciting area is the effects of energy input on
membrane transport. Even though one of the most desirable aspects
of facilitated transport through liquid membranes is the low energy
requirement, the use of electrical or light energy has interesting
consequences. In particular, effective FT for permeates present in
low concentrations requires a large value of $K(eq)$. However, strong
binding of the permeate may result in an unacceptably small value
of $k(r)$. Photochemisty could be used to provide an additional
mechanism for the dissociation of the permeate-carrier complex.
Photodissociation reactions are common for coordination compounds.
Similarly, the electrochemistry associated with the complex could
be used to release permeate on the sweep side of the membrane. The
ability of most metal ions to bind permeates varies with the
oxidation state of the metal. Use of photo- and electrochemical
reactions to enhance FT is depicted in Figure 3. Even though
photofacilitation and electrofacilitation require an energy input,
these processes negate the sole dependence on the properties of
the carrier to provide the selectivity, kinetics and thermodynamics
that are necessary for an efficient separation.

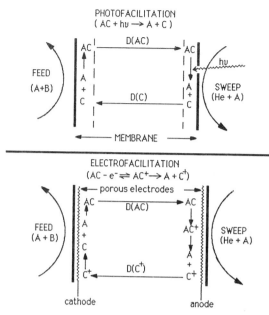

Figure 3. Cross-sectional views depicting processes that result in photofacilitation and electrofacilitation of species A.

Acknowledgments

This paper is based upon research supported by the National Science Foundation under Grant No. CBT-8604518. Acknowledgement is made to the donors of the Petroleum Research Fund, administerd by the American Chemical Society. Z.E.R was supported by a fellowship from the University of Puerto Rico. The authors thank S. Drew, R. Noble, T. Spontarelli and J. Way for useful discussions.

Liturature Cited

1. Gillis, J.N.; Sievers, R.E.; Pollock, G.E. Anal. Chem. 1985, 57, 1572.
2. King, C.J. "Trends in Industrial Separation Processes," First AIChE/CIESC Joint Meeting, Beying, China, 1982.
3. LeBlanc, O.H., Jr.; Ward, W.J.; Matson, S.L.; Kimura, S.G. J. Membr. Sci. 1980, 6, 339.
4. Way, J.D.; Noble, R.D.; Flynn, T.M.; Sloan, E.D. J. Membr. Sci. 1982, 12, 239, and references therein.
5. Warren, D.C. Anal. Chem. 1984, 56, 1523A.
6. Folkner, C.A.; Noble, R.D. J. Membr. Sci. 1983, 12, 289.
7. Kemena, L.L.; Noble, R.D.; Kemp, N.J. J. Membr. Sci. 1983, 15, 259.
8. Scholander, P.F. Science 1960, 131, 585.
9. Kohl, A.L.; Riesenfeld, F.C. Gas Purification; McGraw-Hill: New York, 1970.
10. Smith, D.R.; Quinn, J.A. AIChE. J. 1980, 26, 112.

11. Yukimasa, H.; Sawai, H.; Takizawa, T. Makromol. Chem.
    1979, 180, 1681.
12. Bdzil, B.; Carlier, C.C.; Frisch, H.L.; Ward, W.J. III;
    Breiter, M.W. J. Phys. Chem. 1973, 77, 846.
13. Ward, W.J. III AIChE. J. 1970, 16, 405.
14. Ward, W.J. III Nature 1970, 227, 162.
15. Hartley, F.R. Chem. Rev. 1973, 73, 163.
16. Stynes, D.V.; James, B.R. JACS 1974, 96, 2733.
17. Baldwin, D.A.; Pfeiffer, R.M.; Reichgott, D.W.; Rose, N.J.
    J. Am. Chem. Soc. 1973, 95, 5152.
18. Koval, C.A.; Noble, R.D.; Way, J.D.; Louie, B.; Reyes, Z.E.;
    Bateman, B.R.; Horn, G.M.; Reed, D.L. Inorg. Chem.
    1985, 24, 1147.
19. Bateman, B.R.; Way, J.D.; Larson, K.M. Sep. Sci. Tech.
    1984, 19, 21.
20. Jackels, S.C.; Harris, L.J. Inorg. Syn. 1983, 22, 107.
21. Drago, R.S.; Balkus, K.J. Inorg. Chem. 1986, 25, 718.
22. Nishide, H.; Ohyangi, M.; Okada, O.; Tsuchida, E.
    Macromol. 1986, 19, 496.
23. Nafion is the registered trademark for an IEM produced by
    DuPont deMours, Inc. IEM materials are also available from
    other manufacturers.
24. Elliott, C.M.; Redepenning, J.G. J. Electrochem. Soc.
    1984, 181 137.
25. Way, J.D.; Noble, R.D.; Reid, D.L.; Ginley, G.M.;
    AIChE. J., in press, 1986.
26. Bard, A.J.; Faulkner, L.R. "Electrochemical Methods";
    John Wiley and Sons: New York, 1981, p. 144, 667, 668.
27. Steck, A.; Yeager, H.L. Anal. Chem., 1979, 51, 862.
28. Helfferich, F. "Ion Exchange"; McGraw-Hill:New York; 1961,
    p. 339-420.
29. Lieber, C.M.; Lewis, N.S. J. Am. Chem. Soc. 1985, 107,
    7170.

RECEIVED January 9, 1987

Chapter 3

Separation in Mass-Exchange Devices with Reactive Membranes

Pieter Stroeve and Jong-Inn Kim

Department of Chemical Engineering, University of California at Davis, Davis, CA 95616

Mass transfer rates attainable in membrane separation devices, such as gas permeators or dialyzers,
can be limited by solute transport through the
membrane. The addition into the membrane of a
mobile carrier species, which reacts rapidly and
reversibly with the solute of interest, can
increase the membrane's solute permeability and
selectivity by carrier-facilitated transport. Mass
separation is analyzed for the case of fully developed, one-dimensional, laminar flow of a Newtonian
fluid in a parallel-plate separation device with
reactive membranes. The effect of the diffusion
and reaction parameters on the separation is
investigated. The advantage of using a carrier-
facilitated membrane process is shown to depend on
the wall Sherwood number. When the wall Sherwood
number is below ten, the presence of a carrier-
facilitated membrane system is desirable to improve
solute separation.

Mass and heat transfer with laminar flow in parallel-plate and
cylindrical geometries is a well-known theoretical problem which
has been treated by a large number of investigators (1-9).
Perhaps the first papers in this area were those by Lévêque (1)
and Graetz (2) who studied the heat transfer problem. In the
absence of natural convection and for dilute systems, the heat
and mass transfer problems are analogous.

Parallel plate mass exchange devices with semi-permeable
membranes have been studied in a number of separation techniques
including hemodialysis, artificial oxygenation, gas separation,
and heavy-metal ion separation (10-18). The accurate prediction
of solute separation in these mass exchangers is desirable. For
parallel-plate geometry, Grimsrud and Babb (5) and Colton et al.
(7) developed series solutions to describe the mass transfer
process. Kooijman (8) reviewed the analytical and numerical
solutions available in the early 1970's. Since that time, other

0097-6156/87/0347-0039$06.00/0

analytical solutions to predict the mass transfer performance in
mass exchange devices have appeared (19-23). In general, these
solutions predict a strong dependence of the mass transfer rate
on the wall Sherwood number, Sh_w , of the membrane-fluid system.
The wall Sherwood number is the ratio of the mass transfer
resistance in the fluid to that in the membrane. For $Sh_w = \infty$
the membrane resistance is negligible and the problem reduces to
the classical Graetz problem of a constant concentration boundary
condition (7). For $Sh_w = 0$ the membrane resistance dominates and
the problem has a constant flux boundary condition (24).
     In many cases of practical interest, the membrane's mass
transfer resistance is significant, i.e., the wall Sherwood
number is small, leading to relatively low mass transfer rates
of the solute. The diffusive flux of the permeate through the
membrane can be increased by introducing a carrier species into
the membrane. The augmentation of the flux of a solute by a
mobile carrier species, which reacts reversibly with the solute,
is known as carrier-facilitated transport (25). The use of
carrier-facilitated transport in industrial membrane separation
processes is of considerable interest because of the increased
mass transfer rates for the solute of interest and the improved
selectivity over other solutes (26).
     In this paper, we analyze mass transfer in a parallel-plate
mass exchanger with reactive membranes. We consider the case of
fully developed, one-dimensional laminar flow between two membranes. Equilibrium carrier-facilitated transport of the solute
takes place in the membrane phase. The effect of the diffusion
and reaction parameters of the carrier-facilitated system on
solute separation is investigated.

Theory

A schematic diagram of the system of interest is shown in Fig.
1. The Newtonian fluid, from which solute is to be extracted,
enters the system in fully developed, one-dimensional, laminar
flow. At x = 0, the fluid contacts the reactive membranes. For
immobilized liquid membranes, reactive membranes can be fabricated by dissolving carrier species into an appropriate solvent
and then introducing the solution into a porous membrane support.
Way et al. (27) have discussed the criteria which influence
selection of immobilized liquid membranes containing carrier-
facilitated systems. The carrier species is constrained to
remain in the membrane due to its negligible solubility in the
phases adjacent to the membrane. The solute concentration in the
fluid to be treated is constant and equal to c_i up to the point
it contacts the reactive membranes. As the fluid passes by the
reactive membranes, solute diffuses through the membranes by
carrier-facilitated transport and enters the external or dialyzate fluid. The solute concentration in the dialyzate is assumed
to be zero at all axial positions in the mass exchanger. This is
a reasonable assumption if the incoming dialyzate fluid contains
no solute and if the dialy-zate flow rate is very large compared
to the fluid-side flow rate.

In this paper, we focus on the effect of equilibrium chemical reaction inside the membrane. We consider the common reversible reaction of the form

$$A + B \underset{k_2}{\overset{k_1}{\rightleftharpoons}} AB \tag{1}$$

to take place inside the membrane and with the kinetics suggested by the stochiometry. Here A is the solute, B the carrier and AB the carrier-solute complex species. The chemical reaction rate must be much faster than the diffusion rates for equilibrium to exist and this condition can be expressed by letting the Damköhler number for the diffusion and reaction in the membrane approach infinity (28).

At steady state, the mass conservation equation for the solute species and the associated boundary conditions are expressed as

$$\frac{3}{2} v \left[1 - \left(\frac{y}{h} \right)^2 \right] \frac{\partial c_A}{\partial x} = D_A \frac{\partial^2 c_A}{\partial y^2} \tag{2}$$

B.C.1 $\qquad x = 0, \quad c_A = c_i, \quad$ all y $\qquad\qquad$ (3)

B.C.2 $\qquad y = 0, \quad \dfrac{\partial c_A}{\partial y} = 0, \quad$ all x $\qquad\qquad$ (4)

B.C.3 $\qquad y = h, \quad -D_A \dfrac{\partial c_A}{\partial y} = k_w(1 + F_{eq}) c_A, \quad$ all x $\qquad$ (5)

The term on the right hand side of Eq. (5) represents the total flux of A due to Fickian diffusion and facilitated transport in the flat membrane (28). We have assumed that axial diffusion is negligible compared to axial convection and that no convection takes place across the membrane. The equilibrium facilitation factor, F_{eq}, is given by (28)

$$F_{eq} = \frac{D_B' c_T K_{eq}}{D_A'(1 + K_{eq} c_A H)} \tag{6}$$

when the solute concentration in the dialysate side is zero. The equilibrium constant for reaction (1), K_{eq}, is the ratio of the forward rate to the backward rate constant. The equilibrium distribution coefficient, H, is defined as the ratio of the solute concentration in the membrane to the concentration in the fluid side. Dimensionless variables are now defined as

$$c^* = \frac{c_A}{c_i} \quad , \quad x^* = \frac{xD_A}{Vh^2} \quad , \quad y^* = \frac{y}{h}$$

(7)

$$\alpha = \frac{D_B' c_T K_{eq}}{D_A'} \quad , \quad \beta = K_{eq} H c_i \quad , \quad Sh_w = \frac{hk_w}{D_A}$$

Equations (2) through (5) become

$$\frac{3}{2} (1 - y^{*2}) \frac{\partial c^*}{\partial x^*} = \frac{\partial^2 c^*}{\partial y^{*2}}$$

(8)

B.C.1 $x^* = 0 , \quad c^* = 1, \quad$ all y (9)

B.C.2 $y^* = 0, \quad \frac{\partial c^*}{\partial y} = 0 , \quad$ all x^* (10)

B.C.3 $y^* = 1, \quad -\frac{\partial c^*}{\partial y^*} = Sh_w \left[1 + \frac{\alpha}{1+\beta c^*} \right] c^* , \quad$ all x^* (11)

The parameters Sh_w, α, and β are the wall Sherwood number, the maximum facilitation factor and the dimensionless equilibrium constant. The equilibrium facilitation factor is given as

$$F_{eq} = \frac{\alpha}{1+\beta c^*}$$

(12)

Note that the maximum value that F_{eq} can attain is equal to α. In essence, Sh_w, α and β are the important membrane-fluid and facilitation parameters that influence the mass transfer of the solute from the fluid side to the dialyzate fluid.

Computational Technique

When no reaction takes place in the membrane the parameter α is zero and so is F_{eq}. For the special case of no reaction in the membrane analytical solutions are available in the literature (5, 7, 9, 21). When reaction does take place and $\alpha > 0$, the third boundary condition is nonlinear and to our knowledge no analytical solution to Eqs. (8) through (11) exists. To solve the equations, we used a finite difference Galerkin scheme (with the relaxation parameter set equal to 2/3) (29, 30). Numerical solutions were obtained for c^* as a function of x^* and y^* for different cases of Sh_w, α and β. The mixing cup concentration can be obtained from the solution of c^* and is given at any x^* by

$$c_M^* = \frac{\int_{-1}^{1} c^*(1-y^{*2})dy^*}{\int_{-1}^{1} (1-y^{*2})dy^*} = \frac{\sum_m c_m^*(1-y_m^{*2})\Delta y^*}{\sum_m (1-y_m^{*2})\Delta y^*} \qquad (13)$$

where the summation index runs over the number of numerical grid points spaced between the two membranes. The local, fluid-side Sherwood number at any x^* is given by (7, 31)

$$Sh_{x,f} = -\left.\frac{\frac{\partial c^*}{\partial y^*}}{(c_M^*-c^*)}\right|_{y^*=1} \qquad (14)$$

Both the concentration and the gradient of the concentration are evaluated at the wall ($y^* = 1$). The local, overall Sherwood number at any x^* is (7,31)

$$Sh_{x,o} = -\frac{\left.\frac{\partial c^*}{\partial y^*}\right|_{y^*=1}}{c_M^*} \qquad (15)$$

From additivity of resistances, an equivalent expression yielding identical results is

$$\frac{1}{Sh_{x,o}} = \frac{1}{Sh_{w(1+F_{eq})}} + \frac{1}{Sh_{x,f}} \qquad (16)$$

The dialyzate mass transfer resistance is negligible because of the high flow rate and the zero concentration condition.

Results and Discussion

In order to obtain a stable and convergent solution for c^*, a variety of grid sizes in the finite difference technique were studied. To check the reliability of the numerical results, we compared the calculations to the analytical results given in Colton et al. (7) and Stroeve (31) for the case of no reaction, i.e. $\alpha = 0$. The step size in the x^* direction was found to be 5×10^{-5} and it was 6.25×10^{-3} in the y^* direction. Table 1 reports the mixing cup concentration as a function of the dimensionless length down the exchanger for several wall Sherwood numbers. As shown in the table, in most cases there is excellent agreement between the analytical and numerical results to within three significant figures.

TABLE 1. COMPARISON OF NUMERICAL RESULTS (N) WITH ANALYTICAL
RESULTS (A) AVAILABLE IN THE LITERATURE (7,31) FOR THE CASE
OF NO REACTION INSIDE THE MEMBRANE

| Wall Sherwood Number | Mixing Cup Concentration c_M^* | | | | | |
| | $Sh_w = 0.05$ | | $Sh_w = 1$ | | $Sh_w = 10$ | |
Dimensionless Axial Distance x^*	A	N	A	N	A	N
0.00	0.9999	0.9999	0.9991	0.9993	0.9939	0.9953
0.01	0.9995	0.9995	0.9915	0.9919	0.9646	0.9658
0.1	0.9951	0.9951	0.9282	0.9287	0.8037	0.8052
0.5	0.9758	0.9755	0.7094	0.7089	0.4196	0.4196
1.0	0.9523	0.9516	0.5089	0.5070	0.1880	0.1875
2.5	0.8851	0.8835	0.1870	0.1855	0.0169	0.0167
5.0	0.7834	0.7803	0.0353	0.0347	0.0003	0.0003

When reaction does occur in the membrane, solute transport is
increased and, effectively, the membrane becomes more permeable.
Figure 2 shows the mixing cup concentration as a function of the
dimensionless axial distance for reactive membranes and inert
membranes. The values of α and β are typical and within the
range of optimal values for facilitated transport given by Kemena
et al. (32). Figure 2 clearly shows that solute removal from the
treated fluid is enhanced due to the carrier-facilitated transport
occurring inside the membrane. The curve for $Sh_w = 10$, $\alpha = 10$
and $\beta = 15$ is very close to the results obtained when $Sh_w = \infty$
for no reaction (7,31). For laminar, fully developed, Newtonian
flow the highest separation is obtained for $Sh_w = \infty$. When the
membrane is highly permeable relative to the fluid, the presence of
a reaction in the membrane has no significant effect on mass
transfer.
The effect of changing the value of the dimensionless maximum
facilitation factor, α, and the dimensionless equilibrium constant,
β, is given in Figs. 3 and 4. The mixing cup concentration is
strongly influenced by the value of α. The maximum facilitation
factor can be increased by dissolving more carrier in the membrane

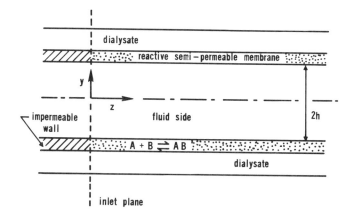

Figure 1. Cross-sectional diagram of parallel plate exchanger with reactive membranes.

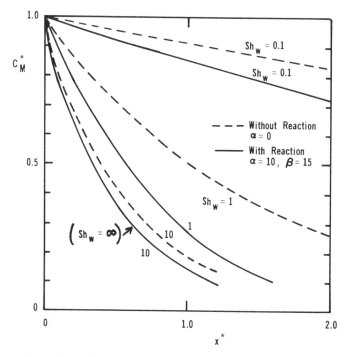

Figure 2. Dimensionless mixing-cup concentration as a function of the dimensionless axial distance and the wall Sherwood number for $\alpha = 10$, $\beta = 15$.

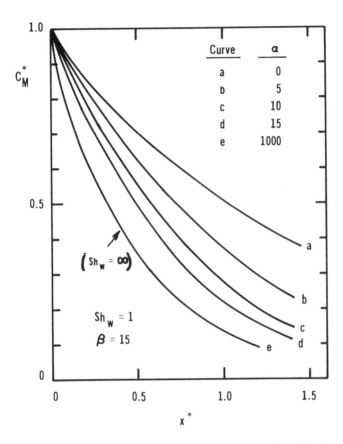

Figure 3. The effect of the maximum facilitation factor on the dimensionless mixing-cup concentration for $Sh_W = 1$, $\beta = 15$.

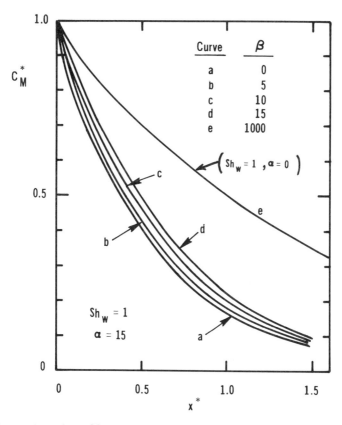

Figure 4.   The effect of dimensionless equilibrium constant on the dimensionless mixing-cup concentration for $Sh_W = 1$, $\alpha = 15$.

which is equivalent to increasing c_T. Figure 2 indicates that
substantial increases in solute removal can be attained for
moderate values of α. As α is further increased an asymptotic
limit is reached. The curve for $\alpha = 1000$ is nearly identical to
the mass separation obtained when $Sh_w = \infty$ for the no reaction
case. For $Sh_w = 1$ and $\beta = 15$ the curves for α greater than
50 are indistinguishable from each other. Increasing β decreases
the separation in the exchanger. Higher values of β reflect
either larger values for the equilibrium constant, the distribution
coefficient or the inlet concentration. The decrease in mass
transfer is due to a saturation effect of the chemical reaction
because of higher solute concentrations on the fluid side. The
mixing cup concentration is less sensitive to changes in β compared to changes in α. For very large values of β , the results
reach the asymptotic limit of the results obtained when no chemical
reaction exists for the specified wall Sherwood number. This is
the situation when the reaction is saturated throughout the membrane
as reaction (1) is completely driven to the right.

As the fluid flows through the exchanger, the concentration of
the solute changes along the membrane. As a consequence, the flux
through the membrane, which is imposed by boundary condition number
three, changes as the equilibrium facilitation factor changes.
Figures 5 and 6 show the dependency of F_{eq} on x^* for different
values of α and β. As the solute wall concentration drops, the
product βc^* in the expression for F_{eq} decreases and the facilitation factor approaches the maximum facilitation factor α .
(There is no contradiction in having F_{eq} increase as solute is
removed; even though F_{eq} becomes larger, the overall solute flux
decreases due to the decrease in the driving force.) The approach
of F_{eq} to the maximum facilitation factor is slower for low wall
Sherwood numbers than for high wall Sherwood numbers. Figure 7
shows the variation of F_{eq} with Sh_w for different dimensionless
axial positions down the exchanger. Although the maximum facilitation in the membrane is obtained at shorter x^* when Sh_w is
large, the impact of the carrier-facilitated transport will be less
significant for Sh_w greater than 10 than for Sh_w less than
10 as shown by Fig. 2.

As expected the chemical reaction in the membrane has a
significant influence of the local, overall Sherwood number and
only a small effect on the local, fluid-side Sherwood number (Figs.
8 and 9). The local, overall Sherwood number as a function of the
wall Sherwood number is plotted in Fig. 8 in the fully developed
region $(x^* \to \infty)$. This is the region where the concentration profile is fully established. Both the reactive and the inert cases
are shown. The effect on $Sh_{x,f}$ is small and is mainly due to
adjustments in the concentration gradient on the fluid side due to
the chemical reaction. There is a large effect on $Sh_{x,o}$ since
the overall membrane resistance to mass transfer is lowered due to
the facilitated transport. In comparison, the result for $x^* = 1$
for the reactive case is also plotted. For the no reaction case,
the local, overall Sherwood number reaches its fully developed value
when $x^* > 0.2$ (7,31), so for $x^* = 1$ the result is identical to
the curve of $x^* = \infty$. The concentration boundary layer develops
slower for the reaction case. As the wall Sherwood number becomes

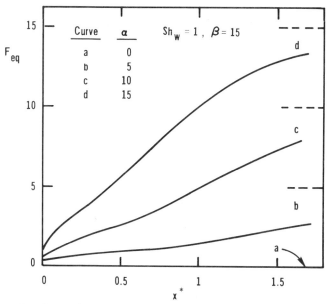

Figure 5.   Dependency of the equilibrium facilitation factor on the dimensionless axial distance and α. The intercept at $x^* = 0$, is $\alpha/(1+\beta)$ for each curve. $Sh_W = 1$, $\beta = 15$.

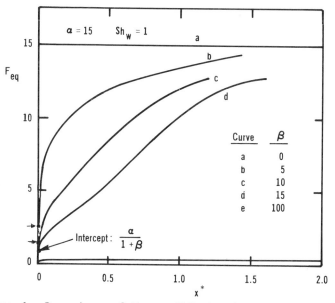

Figure 6.   Dependency of the equilibrium facilitation factor on the dimensionless axial distance and β. The intercept at $x^* = 0$, is $\alpha/(1+\beta)$ for each curve. $Sh_W = 1$, $\alpha = 15$.

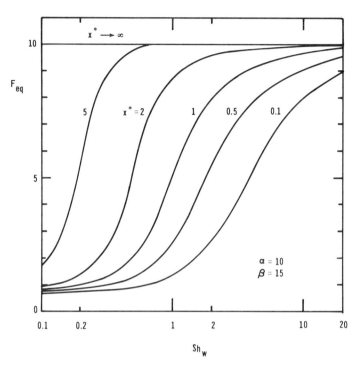

Figure 7.   Equilibrium facilitation factor as a function of the wall Sherwood number and dimensionless axial distance.

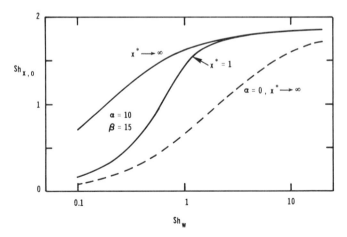

Figure 8.   The local, overall Sherwood number versus the wall Sherwood number for reactive (solid curves) and inert membranes (dashed curve).

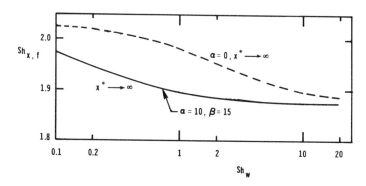

Figure 9. The local, fluid-side Sherwood number versus the wall
Sherwood number for reactive (solid curve) and inert membranes
(dashed curve). Note the expanded scale of the ordinate.

large, the results for the reaction and no reaction cases approach
each other asymptotically. When the membrane is highly permeable,
the effect of facilitated transport is minimal. Figure 10 shows
the role of chemical reaction on the local, overall Sherwood
number in the fully developed regime more dramatically. The ratio,
η , of the fully developed, local, overall Sherwood number for
reaction to the same Sherwood number with no reaction is plotted
as a function of the wall Sherwood number. Whereas substantial
increases can be obtained in the overall Sherwood number due to
carrier-facilitated transport in the membranes for small values
of Sh_W , above $Sh_W = 10$ the effect is minimal. When the wall
Sherwood number has low transport characteristics, $Sh_W < 10$, the
presence of a carrier-facilitated transport system will have
beneficial effects on the mass transfer rates.

The diffusion and reaction parameters for facilitated transport,
i.e. D_A' , D_B' , k_1 and k_2 are not homogeneous, but effective
parameters for the membrane. Immobilized liquid membranes are the
most practical to use in a reactive membrane device. The diffusion
and reaction parameters for a homogeneous liquid will be changed
when the liquid is introduced into a porous polymer support. An
immobilized liquid membrane is a heterogeneous "porous" medium
and effective physical and chemical parameters describe the transport
process occurring inside the system. A variety of theoretical models
have been presented in the literature to predict effective parameters
in heterogeneous media. Volume-averaging is perhaps the most
rigorous approach to obtain effective transport parameters (33-36),
and we are presently using this technique to analyze facilitated
transport in heterogeneous media.

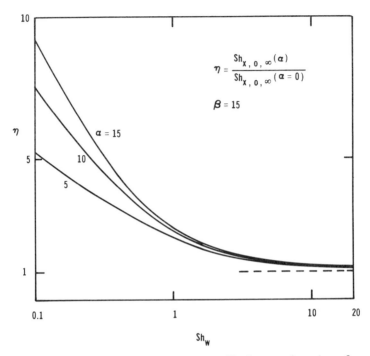

Figure 10. Ratio of the local, overall Sherwood number for reactive membranes to the local, overall Sherwood number for inert membranes in the fully developed regime. The dashed line indicates no enhancement of the overall mass transfer rate. Note that the enhancement ratio η depends on the value of α .

Nomenclature

A   Solute species A

AB   Carrier-solute complex species

B   Species B; uncomplexed carrier species

c_A Concentration of species A

c_i Inlet concentration of species A

c^* Dimensionless concentration of species A

c_M^* Dimensionless mixing-cup concentration

c_T Total concentration of carrier-species in all forms inside the membrane

D_A Diffusivity of species A in fluid

D_A' Effective diffusivity of species A in the reactive membrane

D_B' Effective diffusivity of species B and AB in the reactive membrane

F_{eq} Equilibrium facilitation factor

h   Half-width of channel height

H   Equilibrium distribution coefficient of solute concentration in the membrane to the concentration in the fluid

k_1 Forward rate constant

k_2 Backward rate constant

k_w Membrane mass transfer coefficient

K_{eq} Equilibrium constant for the chemical reaction

$Sh_{x,f}$ Local, fluid-side Sherwood number

$Sh_{x,o}$ Local, overall Sherwood number

Sh_w Wall Sherwood number

V   Average fluid velocity

x   Axial distance

x^* Dimensionless axial distance

y   Coordinate

y^* Dimensionless coordinate

Greek Symbols

α   Maximum facilitation factor

β   Dimensionless equilibrium constant

η   Ratio of local, overall Sherwood numbers for fully-developed laminar flow

Acknowledgment

This study was supported in part by NSF Grant CBT-85 13956.

Literature Cited

1. Lévêque, J. Ann. Mines (Ser. 12), 1928, 13, 201, 305,381.
2. Graetz, L. Ann. Physik, 1885, 25, 337.
3. Prins, J.A.; Mulder, J.; Schenk, J. Appl. Sci. Res., 1950, A2, 431.
4. Van der Does De Bye, J.A.W.; Schenk, J. Appl. Sci. Res. 1952, A3, 308.
5. Grimsrud, L.; Babb, A.L. Chem. Engn. Progr. Symp. Ser. No. 66, 1966, 62, 19.
6. Brown, G.M. AIChE Jour., 1960, 6, 179.
7. Colton, C.K.; Smith, K.A.; Stroeve, P.; Merrill, E.W. AIChE Jour., 1971, 17, 773.
8. Kooijman, J.M. Chem. Engn. Sci., 1973, 28, 1149.
9. Cooney, D.O.; Kim, S.-S.; Davis, E.J. Chem. Engn. Sci., 1974, 29, 1731.
10. Colton, C.K.; Smith, K.A.; Merril, E.W.; Friedman, S. AIChE Jour., 1971, 17, 800.
11. Meares, P. Membrane Separation Processes, Elsevier, Amsterdam, 1976.
12. Oomens, J.M.M.; De Koning, J.; Stroeve, P. AIChE Jour. , 1977, 23, 390.
13. Stroeve, P.; Srinivasan, R. AIChE Jour., 1980, 26, 136.
14. Lonsdale, H.K. J Membr. Sci., 1982, 10, 81.
15. Gardner, R.J.; Crane, R.A.; Hannan, J.F. Chem. Engn. Progr., 1977, 73, 76.
16. Buckles, R.G.; Merrill, E.W.; Gilliland, E.R. AIChE Jour., 1968, 14, 703.
17. Reusch, C.F.; Cussler, E.L. AIChE Jour., 1973, 19, 736.
18. Baker, R.W.; Tuttle, M.E.; Kelly, D.J.; Lonsdale, H.K. J. Membr. Sci., 1977, 2, 213.
19. Davis, E.J. Canad. J. Chem. Engn., 1973, 51, 562.
20. Cooney, D.O.; Davis, E.J.; Kim, S.-S. The Chem. Engn.Jour., 1974, 8, 213.
21. Walker, G.; Davies, T. AIChE Jour., 1974, 20, 881.
22. Chapman, T.W.; Collins, W.W.; Troyer, S.D. AIChE Jour., 1978, 24, 338.
23. Ingham, D.B. Int. J. Heat Transfer, 1984, 27, 2421.
24. Cess, R.D.; Shaffer, E.C. Appl. Sci. Res., 1959, 8, 339.
25. Goddard, J.D.; Schultz, J.S.; Suchdeo, S.R. AIChE Jour., 1974, 20, 625.
26. Kimura, S.G.; Matson, S.L.; Ward, W.J. Rec. Develop. Sep. Sci., 1979, 5, 11.
27. Way, J.D.; Noble, R.D.; Bateman, B.R. In Materials Science of Synthetic Membranes, D.R. Lloyd, Ed., American Chemical Society, Washington, DC., 1985, p. 119.
28. Kreuzer, F.; Hoofd, L.J.C. In Handbook of Physiology IV: Respiration, The American Physiological Society, Washington, DC, in press.
29. Hogge, M.A. In Numerical Methods in Heat Transfer, Lewis, R.W., Morgan, K., and O.C. Zienkiewics, Eds., John Wiley & Sons Ltd., Chichester, England, 1981, p. 75.
30. Mitchell, A.R. Computational Methods in Partial Differential Equations, John Wiley and Sons, Ltd., New York, 1969.

31. Stroeve, P. M.S. Thesis, Massachusetts Institute of Techno-
    logy, Cambridge, MA, 1969.
32. Kemena, L.L.; Noble, R.D.; Kemp, N.J.   J. Membr. Sci., 1983,
    15, 259.
33. Whitaker, S. AIChE Jour., 1967, 13, 240.
34. Slattery, J.C. Momentum, Energy and Mass Transfer in
    Continua, R.E. Krieger Publ., Co., Melbourne, Fl., 1981.
35. Whitaker, S. In Chemical Reactor Analysis: Concepts and
    Design, Whitaker S., Cassano, A.E., Eds., Gordon and Greach,
    New York, 1986.
36. Ochoa, J.A.; Stroeve, P.; Whitaker, S. Chem. Engn. Sci., in
    press, 1986.

RECEIVED January 9, 1987

Chapter 4

Steady-State Coupled Transport of HNO₃ Through a Hollow-Fiber Supported Liquid Membrane

Richard D. Noble[1] and Pier R. Danesi[2,3]

[1]National Bureau of Standards, Center for Chemical Engineering, Boulder, CO 80303
[2]Argonne National Laboratory, Chemistry Division, Argonne, IL 60439

Nitric acid removal from an aqueous stream was accomplished by continuously passing the fluid through a hollow fiber supported liquid membrane (SLM). The nitric acid was extracted through the membrane wall by coupled transport. The system was modeled as a series of (SLM)-continuous stirred tank reactor (CSTR) pairs. An approximate technique was used to predict the steady state nitric acid concentration in the system. The comparison with experimental data was very good.

Mass transfer involving convective transport through a channel and diffusive transport through the channel walls has been previously studied. These studies involved a single pass of fluid through the channel. The channel wall permeability was assumed constant since the transport through the channel wall was purely diffusive and had no reactive component. A major impetus for these studies was the design of blood dialyzers for use as an artificial kidney.

Colton et al. (1) developed a solution for laminar flow in a flat duct with permeable walls. They focused their attention on transport in the entrance region. They also found a simple, approximate technique for estimating the log-mean Sherwood number and mixing cup concentration.

Cooney et al. (2,3) also developed solutions for mass transfer in dialyzers with laminar flow and semi-permeable walls. They provided solutions for both planar and cylindrical configurations.

More recently, Noble (4) developed an analytical solution for two-dimensional transport. The solution allows for facilitated transport through the channel walls. The solution does not account for laminar flow since it assumes that plug flow exists through the channel.

---

[3]Current address: International Atomic Energy Agency, Seibersdorf Laboratories, P.O. Box 200, A-1400 Vienna, Austria

Davis (5) provided exact solutions for a number of mass transfer problems. The details of the method used in this paper and some
of those noted above can be found in this reference.

Experimental

Reagents. The reagents used and their purity were previously described (6-8).

Membrane Systems and Experiments. The transport of nitric acid
through a supported liquid membrane (SLM) containing trilaurylamine
(TLA) as carrier was studied using a single hollow fiber module.
This configuration is similar to one previously reported (9). The
hollow fiber support was a polypropylene tube. The support details
have been described elsewhere (9). The SLM consisted of a 0.1 M
solution of TLA in n-dodecane absorbed into the pores of the hollow
fiber support. The transport properties of the system and the chemical reactions of the nitric acid co-transport have been described at
length (6,7). The feed and strip solutions had the following compositions initially: [HNO₃] = 0.01 M, [NaNO₃] = 1.0 M (feed solution)
and [NaOH] = 1.0 M (strip solution). The hollow fiber module was
operated in a recycling mode at a linear flow velocity of 18 cm/s,
corresponding to a Reynolds number of 346. The volume of the aqueous feed solution which circulated through the membrane lumen was 15
cm³. The volume of the H⁺ concentration detector containing the pH
electrode was 10.7 cm³. The internal volume of the fiber lumen and
the connecting lines was 0.46 cm³ and 3.8 cm³, respectively. The
I.D. of the hollow fiber was 0.172 cm. The volume of the aqueous
strip solution which circulated on the shell side of the SLM was
350 cm³.

Methodology and Results

Figure 1 is a flow diagram of the experimental apparatus. The acidic solution is continuously recirculated through the system. This
continuous recirculation can be approximated by the system shown in
Figure 2. The system is approximated as a series of supported liquid membrane (SLM) - continuous stirred tank reactor (CSTR) pairs.
The time for a single pass through the system (t_t) is

$$t_t = \frac{V_t}{Q} \tag{1}$$

V_t is the transit volume of the system (membrane lumen volume plus
connecting tubing) and Q is the volumetric flowrate through the system. The variable t_t defines the time for 1 cycle in Figure 2.
The governing differential equation which describes the acid
concentration in the SLM is

$$V_{max}\left(1 - \frac{x^2}{R^2}\right) \frac{\partial C}{\partial z} = D_{AB} \frac{1}{x} \frac{\partial}{\partial x}\left(x \frac{\partial C}{\partial x}\right) \tag{2}$$

The boundary conditions are

$$C = C_{i1} \qquad\qquad z=0 \tag{3}$$

$$\frac{\partial C}{\partial x} = 0 \qquad\qquad x=0 \tag{4}$$

$$-D_{AB} \frac{\partial C}{\partial x} = kC \qquad x=R \tag{5}$$

For this experimental system, the sink phase (phase outside the hollow fiber wall) resistance and acid concentration are assumed to be negligible. This is due to the rapid neutralization of the acid by a strong base.

Equations (2) through (5) can be solved to determine the steady state mixing cup outlet concentration (C_{e1}) which exits from the membrane (2).

$$\frac{C_{e1}}{C_{i1}} = \sum_{m=1}^{\infty} B_m \exp(-\lambda_m^2 Z^*) = S \tag{6}$$

To determine S, the following equations are solved (2)

$$(\lambda_m - Sh)\ M\!\left(\frac{2-\lambda_m}{4}, 1, \lambda_m\right) - \lambda_m\!\left(\frac{2-\lambda_m}{2}\right) M\!\left(\frac{6-\lambda_m}{4}, 2, \lambda_m\right) = 0 \tag{7}$$

$$X = \sum_{m=1}^{\infty} X_m = \sum_{m=1}^{\infty} M\!\left(\frac{2-\lambda_m}{4}, 1, \lambda_m x^{*2}\right) \exp\!\left(-\frac{\lambda_m x^{*2}}{2}\right) \tag{8}$$

$$A_m = -\frac{2}{\lambda_m} \frac{\dfrac{dX_m(1)}{dx^*}}{\dfrac{dX_m(1)}{dx^*}\dfrac{dX_m(1)}{d\lambda_m} - X_m(1)\dfrac{d^2X_m(1)}{dx^* d\lambda_m}} \tag{9}$$

$$B_m = -\frac{4A_m}{\lambda_m^2} \frac{dX_m(1)}{dx^*} \tag{10}$$

$$x^* = \frac{x}{R}, \quad Z^* = \frac{z}{R\ Pe}, \quad Pe = \frac{v_{max}\ R}{D_{AB}} \tag{11}$$

where λ_m = eigenvalues for equation (7)

        M = confluent hypergeometric function

       Sh = wall Sherwood number

$$= \frac{k\ R}{D_{AB}}$$

k = overall mass transfer coefficient for the membrane and sink phase.

$X_m(1) = X_m$ evaluated at $x^* = 1$

A mass balance around the CSTR is

$$V_c \frac{dC_i}{dt} = Q(C_{e1} - C_{i1}) \qquad (12)$$

V_c is the CSTR volume. The derivative can be approximated at long times by

$$\frac{dC_i}{dt} \cong \frac{C_{i2} - C_{i1}}{V_t/Q} \qquad (13)$$

Equations (6), (12), and (13) can be combined to yield

$$\frac{C_{i2}}{C_{i1}} = 1 - V^* (1 - S) \qquad (14)$$

where

$$V^* = \frac{V_t}{V_c} \qquad (15)$$

Repeating this analysis through n cycles, one obtains

$$\frac{C_{in}}{C_{i1}} = \left[1 - V^* (1 - S) \right]^{n-1} \qquad (16)$$

The time dependence in Equation 16 is determined by n. The time corresponding to C_{in} is $(n-1)t_t$. Once S is determined, the steady state concentration change can be calculated. This requires knowledge of Sh. The variable k can be viewed as an effective diffusion coefficient for the acid-carrier complex divided by the membrane thickness. Since the acid concentration changes with time, the actual Sh will vary. Therefore, the Sh was estimated for one value of n and the resulting S value was used in Equation 16.

The comparison of experimental results with the predictions of Equation 16 is shown in Figure 3. The parameters used in the calculation are listed in Figure 3. The Sh number was estimated using a value of n=20. As seen from the figure, the agreement between the method and experiment is very good. This is due to the fact that the Sh number is large and invariant in this case. The nonlinear portion of the curve in Figure 3 is due to the transient response of the system. This transient time is associated with the characteristic diffusion time through the membrane wall. This time is much larger than t_t.

The theoretical results can be useful in the following ways. Once a system was calibrated to estimate Sh, extraction rates can be calculated. This allows one to determine the time required to reduce the acid concentration to a desirable value. Secondly, the

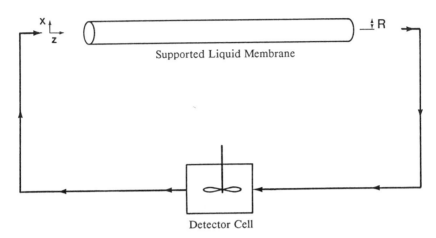

Figure 1.   Flow Diagram for the Experimental Apparatus

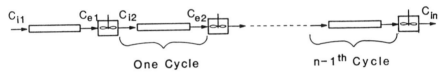

Figure 2.   System Approximated as a Series of SLM-CSTR Pairs

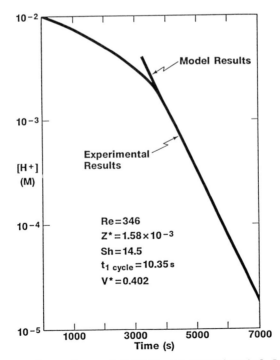

Figure 3.   Comparison of Method and Experimental Results

effect of changes in system variables can be estimated. This includes changes in membrane length (Z^*), flow through the system (Pe), and membrane radius (x^* and Z^*).

The major advantage of this method is the analytical solution for the steady state acid concentration in the system. This allows simple and rapid estimation of extraction rates and the effect of changes in system variables on system performance.

The main disadvantage is the requirement to estimate Sh. A more rigorous solution would allow for the variation of Sh. This would require a numerical method for a solution. See the chapter entitled "Separation in Mass Exchange Devices with Reactive Membranes" by Stroeve and Kim (10) in this volume for an example of this rigorous approach.

Conclusions

An approximate analytical solution has been developed to calculate the exit concentration from a continuously recirculating facilitated transport liquid membrane system. The system is modeled as a series of SLM-CSTR pairs. The solution allows for two-dimensional transport (axial convective and radial diffusive) and laminar flow. The solution allows one to estimate the effect of a change in system variables on the operating performance. Comparison with experimental data was very good.

Literature Cited

1. Colton, C.K.; Smith, K.A.; Stroeve, P.; Merril, E.W., A.I.Ch.E. J. 1971, 17(4), 773.
2. Cooney, D.O.; Kim, S.S.; Davis, E.J. Chem. Eng. Sci. 1974, 29, 1731.
3. Cooney, D.O.; Davis, E.J.; Kim. S.S. Chem. Eng. Sci. 1974, 8, 213.
4. Noble, R.D. Sep. Sci. Tech. 1984, 19(8&9), 469.
5. Davis,E.J. Canadian J. Chem. Eng. 1973, 51, 562.
6. Cianetti, C.; Danesi, P.R. Solvent Extr. Ion Exch. 1983, 1, 565.
7. Danesi, P.R.; Cianetti, C.; Horwitz, E.P. Solvent Extr. Ion Exch. 1983, 1(2), 299.
8. Danesi, P.R.; Reichley-Yinger, L.; Cianetti, C.; Rickert, R.G. Solvent Extr. Ion Exch. 1984, 2, 781.
9. Danesi, P.R.; Chiarizia, R.; Rickert, P.G.; Horwitz, E.P. Solvent Extr. Ion Exch. 1985, 3, 111.
10. Stroeve, P.; Kim, J. In Liquid Membranes: Theory and Applications; Noble, R.D.; Way, J.D., Eds.; American Chemical Society: Washington, D.C., 1987.

RECEIVED April 20, 1987

Chapter 5

Influence of Reaction Reversibility on Continuous-Flow Extraction by Emulsion Liquid Membranes

D. L. Reed[1], A. L. Bunge[1,3], and R. D. Noble[2]

[1]Colorado School of Mines, Golden, CO 80401
[2]National Bureau of Standards, Center for Chemical Engineering, Boulder, CO 80303

This paper examines theoretically the continuous flow extraction by emulsion globules in which the transferring solute reacts with an internal reagent. The reversible reaction model is used to predict performance. These results are compared with advancing front calculations which assume an irreversible reaction. A simple criterion which indicates the importance of reaction reversibility on performance is described. Calculations show that assuming an irreversible reaction can lead to serious underdesign when low solute concentrations are required. For low solute concentrations an exact analytical solution to the reversible reaction problem is possible. For moderate solute concentrations, we have developed an easy parameter adjustment of the advancing front model which reasonably approximates expected extraction rates.

Emulsion liquid membranes (ELM) are double emulsions formed by mixing two immiscible phases and then dispersing the resulting emulsion in another continuous phase under agitation. Proposed applications for emulsion liquid membranes have included selective recovery of metal ions (1-12), separation of hydrocarbons (13-16), removal of trace organic contaminants (17-27), and encapsulation of reactive enzymes or whole cells (28-36).

Nearly all of the large number of experimental and theoretical studies reported have been performed in batch mode. While the industrial significance of a continuous steady-state operation is obvious, only Hatton and coworkers have examined flow configurations both theoretically and experimentally (27,37,38). They considered the situation when a solute (A) diffuses through the oil phase membrane and then reacts with a reagent (B) trapped in the internal droplets to produce a product (P) according to,

$$A + B \underset{\longleftarrow}{\overset{K}{\longrightarrow}} P \tag{1}$$

[3]To whom correspondence should be sent

The product is insoluble in the membrane phase and trapped in the internal droplets along with any unreacted reagent. This scheme permits accumulation of reacted solute within the internal phase droplets at significantly larger concentrations than the original solute concentration in the feed.

Examples of such an ELM system are the extraction of organic bases by acidified internal droplets or the extraction of acids by basic droplets. Experimental results for a continuous internal recycle reactor have been reported for ammonia extraction using a sulfuric acid internal phase (27).

To design large scale extractors from bench scale data requires predictive models which describe the physicochemical processes operating in an ELM extraction unit correctly. Many of the models proposed to describe ELM extractions have limited utility since several parameters cannot be determined independently. An important exception is the advancing front model presented by Ho et al. (26) and Hatton et al. (27). They consider the operation as a diffusion-controlled extraction coupled with an instantaneous reaction when K is infinite. The resulting species continuity equation is solved with a perturbation technique producing several algebraic expressions which depend only on independently measurable-physical and operating parameters. Hatton and coworkers use the zero-order solution of the advancing front theory to analyze their continuous ammonia extraction experiments and to predict multistage performance of mixer-settler trains and cascade mixers (27,37,38).

Recently, Bunge and Noble (39) have extended the approach of Ho et al. (26) to include reversibility of reaction 1. Batch extractions and calculations from this reversible reaction model demonstrate that reaction reversibility significantly affects extraction performance in some cases (39,40). In this paper, we extend these batch extraction calculations to a continuous stirred-tank extractor. We show that a single, dimensionless parameter can be used to assess the likely contribution of reversibility for a given set of conditions.

Continuous Stirred-Tank Extractor Design

Figure 1 diagrams a continuous stirred-tank extractor and indicates the pertinent design parameters. In a well-stirred, steady-state extractor, the bulk phase concentration of solute is uniform throughout the tank and equal to the constant outlet concentration, C_{Ab}^{o}. The bulk phase feed enters the extractor at a concentration C_{AB}^{i} and a volumetric flowrate, v_b. The emulsion phase is made from an internal phase solution of reagent, C_{Bi}^{i}, and a solute-free membrane phase. The volume fraction of membrane phase to total emulsion is denoted as f_m. If some of the spent emulsion is recycled through the emulsifier, the average membrane phase concentration of solute fed to the extractor, C_{Am}^{i}, will be nonzero. The volumetric flowrate of the emulsion phase is v_e. The volume of bulk and emulsion phases in the extractor are V_b and V_e, respectively. For steady-state operation of the stirred extractor in Figure 1, the flow ratio of feed to emulsion, v_b/v_e, will usually equal the volume ratio, V_b/V_e.

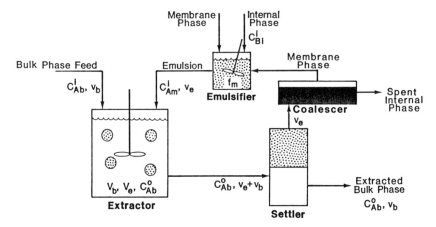

Figure 1 - Schematic diagram of a continuous flow extraction
using emulsion liquid membranes

Four design parameters can be varied independently to achieve a desired degree of solute extraction: the fraction of the emulsion which is membrane phase (f_m), the initial concentration of reagent in the internal phase (C_{Bi}^i), the feed ratio of bulk phase to emulsion phase (v_b/v_e), and the residence time of the emulsion ($t_e = V_e/v_e$). That is, the extent of globule utilization depends on the mass of reagent available and the exposure time of the emulsion to the bulk phase solution. These same four criteria fully specify the design even for an alternate extractor configuration, such as Hatton's continuous internal recycle mixer, which permits $v_b/v_e \neq V_b/V_e$ or equivalently $t_e \neq t_b = V_b/v_b$. We show later that varying the hold-up ratio (V_b/V_e) while keeping f_m, C_{Bi}^i, v_b/v_e and t_e constant does not affect the amount of extraction.

Emulsion Liquid Membrane Models

To estimate the extent of globule utilization for a given exposure time requires a mathematical description of a diffusion-controlled extraction coupled with chemical reaction. Two approaches, the reversible reaction model (39), and the advancing front model (27), will be described and compared.

Basic assumptions in both models include: (1) membrane/bulk and membrane/internal phases are immiscible, (2) local phase equilibrium between membrane and internal phases, (3) no internal circulation in the globule, (4) uniform globule size, (5) mass transfer is controlled by globule diffusion, (6) internal droplets are solute sinks with finite capacity, (7) reaction of solute in the internal phase is instantaneous, (8) no coalescence and redistribution of globules, and (9) a well-mixed tank with an exponential residence time distribution of emulsion globules.

Of these, assumption 8 may seem the most daring. If coalescence and redistribution were extensive, the emulsion globules would approach the limit of uniform solute concentration and diffusive resistances within the globule would not contribute to extraction rates. However, experimental observations indicate that once formed, globules tend to retain their identities. When globules do coalesce and break, undesirable leakage of internal droplets into the bulk phase results. Consequently, preferred globule formulations minimize breakage and recoalescence, thereby assuring applicability of assumption 8.

The sole difference between the advancing front and reversible reaction approach is the assumed size of the equilibrium constant for reaction 1. Advancing front models assume that reaction 1 is irreversible; K is infinitely large. Finite values for K are assumed in the reversible reaction theory.

Reversible Reaction Model.
In an ideal, continuous-stirred extractor, the solute concentration of the bulk phase is uniform and equal to the outlet concentration, C_{Ab}^o. The solute concentration in the membrane portion of the globule, C_{Am}, is given as (39-41):

$$\frac{\partial C_{Am}}{\partial t} = \frac{\bar{D}_{eff}}{r^2} \frac{\partial}{\partial r} \left(r^2 \frac{\partial C_{Am}}{\partial r} \right) - \left(\frac{1-f_m}{f_m} \right) \left(\frac{\partial C_{Ai}}{\partial t} + \frac{\partial C_{Pi}}{\partial t} \right) \qquad (2)$$

$$t = 0 \qquad\qquad C_{Am} = C_{Am}^i \qquad\qquad (R > r \geq 0) \qquad (3)$$

$$r = R \qquad\qquad C_{Am} = K_{mb} C_{Ab}^o \qquad\qquad (t \geq 0) \qquad (4)$$

$$r = 0 \qquad\qquad \frac{\partial C_{Am}}{\partial r} = 0 \qquad\qquad (\text{for all } t) \qquad (5)$$

where R is the globule radius, K_{mb} is the solute partition coefficient between the membrane and bulk phases and f_m is the volume fraction of the globule occupied by the membrane phase. For a composite medium like an emulsion globule, the mean effective diffusion coefficient, $\bar{D}_{eff}$, based on the membrane driving force, includes diffusion of both reacted and unreacted solute through the internal phase in addition to solute diffusion through the membrane phase (24, 25, 39).

The initial condition, Equation 3, assumes that the membrane concentration is uniform with position at C_{Am}^i. For a fresh emulsion feed, C_{Am}^i is zero; nonzero values for C_{Am}^i arise when previously contacted emulsion is thoroughly mixed and reintroduced. Nonzero values also occur whenever the solute is soluble in the membrane phase and the membrane phase is reused as shown in Figure 1.

The concentrations of solute A and product P in the internal phase, C_{Ai} and C_{Pi}, are restricted by reagent conservation and phase and reaction equilibria:

$$C_{Ai} = C_{Am}/K_{mi} \qquad (6)$$

$$C_{Pi} = \frac{K C_{Ai} C_{Bi}^i}{1+K C_{Ai}} \qquad (7)$$

where C_{Bi}^i is the initial concentration of reagent B in the internal phase droplets, and K_{mi} is the solute partition coefficient between the membrane and internal phases, assumed to be constant. If equilibrium between the membrane and internal phase is achieved instantaneously, and using the following definitions,

$$\eta = \frac{r}{R} \quad ; \quad \tau = \frac{D_{eff,NR} \; t}{R^2} \qquad (8)$$

$$\phi_m = \frac{C_{Am}}{C_{Ab}^o K_{mb}} \qquad (9)$$

$$\sigma_1^+ = f_m \frac{v_e}{v_b} K_{mb} \qquad (10)$$

$$\sigma_2^+ = (1-f_m) \frac{v_e}{v_b} \frac{K_{mb}}{K_{mi}} \tag{11}$$

$$\sigma_3 = K C_{Bi}^i \tag{12}$$

$$\sigma_4^0 = K K_{mb} C_{Ab}^0 / K_{mi} \tag{13}$$

$$\lambda = \bar{D}_{eff} / D_{eff,NR} \tag{14}$$

Equations 2-5 become:

$$\frac{\partial \phi_m}{\partial \tau} = \frac{\lambda}{\eta^2} \frac{\partial}{\partial \eta} \left(\eta^2 \frac{\partial \phi_m}{\partial \eta} \right) \left[\frac{1}{1 + (\sigma_2^+ / \sigma_1^+)[1 + \sigma_3/(1 + \sigma_4^0 \phi_m)^2]} \right] \tag{15}$$

$$\tau = 0 \qquad \phi_m = \phi_m^i \qquad 1 > \eta \geqq 0 \tag{16}$$

$$\eta = 1 \qquad \phi_m = 1 \qquad \tau \geqq 0 \tag{17}$$

$$\eta = 0 \qquad \frac{\partial \phi_m}{\partial \eta} = 0 \qquad \text{for all } \tau \tag{18}$$

The plus sign on σ_1^+ and σ_2^+ distinguishes these definitions from σ_1 and σ_2 presented in previous papers on batch extraction (39-41), which are based on the volume ratio (V_e/V_b) rather than the ratio of volumetric flow rates (v_e/v_b). The distinction between batch and continuous extractors is only important when the ratio of volumetric flowrates (v_e/v_b) differ from the extractor volume ratio (V_e/V_b). The definitions for σ_1 and σ_1^+ as well as σ_2 and σ_2^+ become identical for operations restricted to $v_e/v_b = V_e/V_b$.

The ratio of the mean effective diffusion coefficient when reactions occur, $\bar{D}_{eff}$, to the diffusion coefficient when there is no reaction, $D_{eff,NR}$, is estimated using the Jefferson-Witzell-Sibbett equation (42,43) for a composite media and correcting for solute reaction in the internal phase:

$$\lambda = \frac{\int_{\phi_m^i}^{1} D_{eff,R} \, d\phi_m}{D_{eff,NR}} \tag{19}$$

$$D_{eff,k} = D_m \left[1 - \frac{\pi}{4(1+2p)^2} \right] + \frac{\pi}{4(1+2p)} \left[\frac{D_{Fk} D_m}{D_m + 2pD_{Fk}} \right] , \quad k=R \text{ or } NR \quad (20)$$

$$D_{F,k} = \frac{2 (D_i \gamma_k / K_{mi}) D_m}{(D_i \gamma_k / K_{mi}) - D_m} \left[\left(\frac{D_i \gamma_k / K_{mi}}{D_i \gamma_k / K_{mi} - D_m} \right) \ln \left(\frac{D_i \gamma_k}{K_{mi} D_m} \right) -1 \right] , \quad k=R \text{ or } NR \quad (21)$$

$$p = 0.403 (1 - f_m)^{-1/3} - 0.5 \quad (22)$$

$$\gamma_R = 1 + \frac{\sigma_3}{(1+\sigma_4^0 \phi_m)^2} \quad \text{and} \quad \gamma_{NR} = 1 \quad (23)$$

Equation 19 determines the mean value of the reaction-influenced to nonreaction diffusion coefficient ratio between the inlet and maximum membrane concentrations. Derivation and discussion of Equations 19 through 23 are detailed elsewhere (39,40).

Advancing Front Model.   The advancing front model follows a similar approach except that solute diffusion only occurs through the fully reacted outer shell. The no-reaction effective diffusion coefficient, $D_{eff,NR}$, applies in this case. The solute concentration is zero at the dimensionless location of the reaction front, χ, which moves from the globule surface ($\chi=1$) toward the globule center.
Hatton et al. (27) presented the zero-order or pseudosteady-state solution for the advancing front theory, described here in our nomenclature:

$$\phi_m = \frac{1}{\eta} \left[\frac{\eta-\chi}{1-\chi} \right] \quad (24)$$

$$\left. \frac{\partial \phi_m}{\partial \eta} \right|_{\eta=1} = \frac{\chi}{1-\chi} \quad (25)$$

$$\tau = \frac{\sigma_2^+ \sigma_3 (1- 3\chi^2 + 2\chi^3)}{6\sigma_1^+ \sigma_4^0} \quad (26)$$

which applies when C_{Am}^i is zero and the condition

$$\sigma_2^+ \sigma_3 \gg \sigma_4^0 (\sigma_1^+ + \sigma_2^+) \quad (27)$$

is met. Equation 27 states in dimensionless form that the capacity of the globule for a reaction-based extraction, measured by the reagent concentration and internal phase volume, far exceeds the capacity of the globule for extraction by solubility alone. This restriction can be relaxed by including additional terms in the perturbation series (26).

Continuous Stirred-Tank Extraction

The overall solute transfer rate, $\dot{m}_A$, must be related to the solute flux into the globules present as:

$$\dot{m}_A = v_b \left(c_{Ab}^i - c_{Ab}^o \right) = \int_0^{N_T} 4\pi R^2 \bar{D}_{eff} \; f_m \left. \frac{\partial C_{Am}}{\partial r} \right|_{r=R} dn(t) \qquad (28)$$

where N_T is the total number of globules in the extractor, and $n(t)$ is the number of globules with residence times larger than t. The diameter of all globules is assumed to be 2R. For a well-mixed tank, the globule residence time distribution is described as

$$\frac{n(t)}{N_T} = e^{-t/t_e} \qquad (29)$$

with t_e, the average emulsion residence, equal to the ratio of the volume of emulsion in the tank, V_e, to the emulsion volumetric flow rate, v_e. After an overall mass balance on the emulsion, Equation 28 in dimensionless form becomes:

$$\sigma_4^i - \sigma_4^o = 3\lambda \sigma_4^o \sigma_1^+ \int_0^\infty \left. \frac{\partial \phi_m}{\partial \eta} \right|_{\eta=1} e^{-\tau/\tau_e} \; d\tau \qquad (30)$$

where τ_e represents the dimensionless emulsion residence time:

$$\tau_e = \frac{D_{eff,NR}}{R^2} t_e = \frac{D_{eff,NR}}{R^2} \frac{V_e}{v_e} \qquad (31)$$

and the dimensionless inlet concentration, $\sigma_4^i = K \, K_{mb} \, C_{Ab}^i / K_{mi}$. The quantity $(\sigma_4^i - \sigma_4^o)$ represents the dimensionless capacity of the extractor at a given residence time. Equation 30 is used to predict the inlet solute concentration which can be handled for a given set of design parameters: σ_1^+, σ_2^+/σ_1^+, σ_3, σ_4^o and τ_e which correspond respectively to v_e/v_b, f_m, C_{Bi}^i, C_{Ab}^o, and V_e/v_e.

The nonlinearity in Equation 15 disappears when σ_4^o is small, permitting an analytical solution for the surface flux:

$$\left. \frac{\partial \phi_m}{\partial \eta} \right|_{\eta=1} = 2 \sum_{n=1}^\infty \exp \left[- \frac{n^2 \pi^2 \sigma_1^+ \tau}{\sigma_1^+ + \sigma_2^+ (1 + \sigma_3)} \right] \qquad (32)$$

Substituting Equation 32 into Equation 30 produces the following algebraic solution:

$$\sigma_4^i - \sigma_4^o = 6 \sigma_1^+ \sigma_4^o \tau_e \sum_{n=1}^\infty \left[1 + \frac{n^2 \pi^2 \sigma_1 \tau_e}{\sigma_1^+ + \sigma_2^+ (1 + \sigma_3)} \right]^{-1} \qquad (33)$$

Equation 33 represents an exact solution whenever the quantity $(1 + \sigma_4^o)$ is approximately one.

The advancing front calculations require substitution of Equations 25 and 26 into Equation 30 to yield ($\underline{27}$):

$$\sigma_4^i - \sigma_4^o = 3\sigma_2^+\sigma_3 \int_0^1 \chi^2 \exp\left[-\frac{\sigma_2^+\sigma_3(1-3\chi^2+2\chi^3)}{6\sigma_1^+ \sigma_4^o \tau_e}\right] d\chi \qquad (34)$$

which is numerically integrated. The no-reaction diffusion coefficient is appropriate in the advancing front theory and consequently Equation 34 is written for $\lambda = 1$. According to Equation 34 the globule capacity for extraction is zero when the reagent concentration, σ_3, is zero. This is consistent with the restriction of Equation 27 which limits extraction to the solute which reacts.

The advancing front and reversible reaction models both predict that the amount of extraction depends on the emulsion residence time and the ratio of emulsion and bulk phase feed rates, v_e/v_b, as measured by the dimensionless group σ_1^+. No independent dependence on the hold-up ratio, V_e/V_b, is indicated. For extractor designs which permit V_e/V_b to differ from v_e/v_b, model calculations predict that the amount of extraction should be independent of the hold-up ratio if v_e/v_b, τ_e and C_{Ab}^o are fixed. This was observed in experiments with the internal reflux reactor described by Hatton and coworkers ($\underline{27}$).

The maximum inlet concentration of solute which can be reduced to a required outlet concentration can be determined from an overall solute balance at equilibrium conditions. Assuming that only fresh emulsion is used (that is, $C_{Am}^i = 0$) and including reaction reversibility:

$$\left(\sigma_{4,max}^i - \sigma_4^o\right)_{RR} = \sigma_4^o(\sigma_1^+ + \sigma_2^+) + \sigma_3\sigma_2^+\sigma_4^o/(1 + \sigma_4^o) \qquad (35)$$

The assumption of an irreversible reaction requires that the maximum concentration of reacted solute in the internal phase equal the original concentration of reagent, C_{Bi}^i. When reaction 1 is irreversible and C_{Am}^i is zero, the maximum σ_4^i which can be treated is:

$$\left(\sigma_{4,max}^i - \sigma^o\right)_{AF} = \sigma_4^o(\sigma_1^+ + \sigma_2^+) + \sigma_3\sigma_2^+ \qquad (36)$$

If the requirement of Equation 27 is met, then the globule capacity for extraction, $(\sigma_{4,max}^i - \sigma_4^o)$, equals the capacity for reaction alone, $\sigma_2^+\sigma_3$.

Comparing Equations 35 and 36, we see that the deviation of $(1+\sigma_4^o)/\sigma_4^o$ from 1 measures the ability of a given bulk phase solute concentration to drive reaction 1 to completion. Consequently, the simpler advancing front approach is sufficient when the dimensionless concentration of solute in the extractor is large. One complication is that at large σ_4^o the contribution of phase equilibrium to the extent of extraction increases, meaning that the pseudo-

steadystate restriction, Equation 27, cannot be met. For small
values of σ_4^o, reaction reversibility needs to be considered.

Since the normalized advancing front model is adequate except
for small σ_4^o values, a legitimate question is whether σ_4^o of 1.0
or less is likely to occur. Table I shows reaction equilibrium
constants for several acidic and basic compounds and concentrations
corresponding to $\sigma_4^o = 1$. Values of σ_4^o when solute concentrations
are 1 ppm are also tabulated. Clearly, removal of trace organic
acids or bases with small reaction constants can lead to small
σ_4^o values.

An alternate way of evaluating extractor performance is to
measure the extent to which the emulsion capacity is utilized. We
define the fractional utilization of the emulsion as:

$$F_e = \frac{\sigma_4^i - \sigma_4^o}{\sigma_{4,max}^i - \sigma_4^o} \tag{37}$$

For example, brief exposure times will use only a small fraction of
the emulsion capacity for extraction. Long emulsion residence
times will allow nearly complete equilibration with the bulk phase
solution and force F_e to approach 1 asymptotically.

Results and Discussion

Results of sample calculations are shown in Figures 2 through 5.
These results are based on typical operating and physical parameters: a fresh emulsion feed ($C_{Am}^i = 0$), a globule membrane
fraction (f_m) of 0.6 and a value of 1.0 for both distribution
coefficients (K_{mb} and K_{mi}).

Figure 2 reports the dimensionless extractor capacity for
various values of the dimensionless solute concentration leaving
the extractor (σ_4^o). The mass of reagent available for reaction
is constant and specified by σ_3 of 2000 and v_b/v_e of 9.0. The
solid curves denote predictions of the reversible reaction theory
given in Equation 30; the broken curves are predictions of the advancing front model, Equation 34. For a given dimensionless outlet
concentration, increasing the average residence time for the emulsion globules increases the solute feed concentration which can be
treated.

Extractor Design. Data such as those shown in Figure 2 are required for extractor design. Except for the emulsion residence
time, operating parameters are fixed by factors other than the desired amount of extraction. For example, the fraction of membrane
phase in the emulsion and the reagent concentration will generally
be controlled by emulsion durability and the concentration of reacted solute desired. The ratio of feed-to-emulsion flow rate will
depend on mixing considerations. Smaller ratios of v_b/v_e increase
the amount of solute which can be extracted for a given volume of
bulk phase feed. However, as the volume ratio of bulk phase to
emulsion decreases, thorough mixing becomes more difficult. A lower limit of v_b/v_e equal to 0.35 corresponds to uniform close-packed

spheres of emulsion surrounded by bulk solution (i.e., fraction of
voids between emulsion globules is 0.26). Realistically, v_b/v_e
values of less than 1.0 are probably not practical.

To complete the design requires specification of the extractor
size, which is determined from the τ_e required to reach a given
amount of extraction. The information required are the dimensionless solute concentration of the bulk phase feed σ_4^f, and the
dimensionless solute concentration which must be reached, σ_4^o.
The τ_e needed to extract ($\sigma_4^f - \sigma_4^o$) can be read from the ($\sigma_4^i - \sigma_4^o$)
curve for the specified σ_4^o. Using the conditions in Figure 2
and assuming σ_4^f and σ_4^o to be respectively 50 to 10, the advancing front and reversible reaction models both predict a τ_e of about
3. This result corresponds to 12.5 minutes for typical values of
the average globule diameter (1.0 mm) and the effective diffusion
coefficient ($10^{-9}m^2/s$).

According to the reversible reaction prediction, a σ_4^f of 20
and σ_4^o of 1 can be reached with one extractor sized to give a τ_e
of 25 (typically about 100 minutes). The advancing front curve
predicts a much smaller τ_e could accomplish this same separation.
By contrast, the advancing front model curve indicates that the
extraction ($\sigma_4^f - \sigma_4^o$) of (200-100) is not possible in a single
stage; the reversible reaction model shows a τ_e of 100 should work.

If the ($\sigma_4^i - \sigma_4^o$) curve does not reach the value for the desired ($\sigma_4^f-\sigma_4^o$), then the globule capacity is insufficient to
achieve the required separation in a single extraction unit. If
fresh emulsion is delivered to all extractors of a multistage
scheme, commonly called a cross-flow configuration, then the information in Figure 2 remains applicable. In an alternate scheme for
the σ_4^f of 20 and σ_4^o of 1, one extractor could reduce the feed
to a σ_4^o of 10 (requiring a τ_e of about 0.12 or 0.5 minutes).
This becomes the feed to a second extractor which needs a τ_e of
approximately 2.5 (about 11 minutes) to complete the extraction to
($\sigma_4^i - \sigma_4^o$) = (10-1). In this example, the total extractor volume
for the two-stage scheme is considerably less than the one stage
design. However, some of the capital savings would be offset by
the additional pumps, piping and the second bulk phase-emulsion
settler which would be required.

A countercurrent, cascade-type configuration would increase
the emulsion capacity for solute extraction. In this situation,
the emulsion from the second (small σ_4^o) stage becomes the emulsion feed to the first (large σ_4^o) stage. To determine the residence time of the high concentration stage requires generation of
curves like those in Figure 2, but calculated for the average solute concentration of the emulsion leaving the low concentration
stage. The average solute membrane concentration from the dilute
stage depends on the mass of solute extracted according to

$$\frac{\sigma_4^i}{\sigma_4^o} - 1 = \phi_m^i \left[\sigma_1^+ + \sigma_2^+ + \frac{\sigma_2^+ \sigma_3}{1 + \sigma_4^o \phi_m^i} \right] \qquad (38)$$

For a series of countercurrent extractors, the interstage membrane
solute concentration can be calculated from a slightly modified
Equation 38.

Reversibility Effects. Figure 2 demonstrates that differences between advancing front and reversible reaction model predictions are
significant when σ_4^o is less than 1 or when σ_4^o is greater than 10.
When σ_4^o is small, as measured by the deviation of $(1+\sigma_4^o)/\sigma_4^o$ from
1, the solute concentration is too small to force the reagent to
react completely. Reaction reversibility causes the globule
extraction capacity to depend on the outlet solute concentration.
    Table II summarizes the maximum extraction capacities which
correspond to the plateau values in Figure 2. These numbers are
calculated using Equations 35, 36 and Equation 36 restricted by
Equation 27. When reactions are reversible, the globule capacity
for extraction increases as σ_4^o increases. If reaction 1 is irreversible, all of the reagent will react independent of solute
concentration. Small differences in the advancing front's total
capacity at different σ_4^o values arise from the solubility of
unreacted solute solubility in the membrane and internal phases.
When σ_4^o is small, reaction reversibility becomes significant,
making some extractions impossible to accomplish in a single unit.
    As σ_4^o increases to 10 and $(1+\sigma_4^o)/\sigma_4^o$ becomes more nearly
equal to 1, the differences between the advancing front and reversible reaction results disappear. But when σ_4^o is 100 the predicted
reversible reaction capacity exceeds values calculated by the advancing front model. This difference is a consequence of the restriction for the pseudosteady-state solution, Equation 27, which
considers solute reaction as the sole contributor to extraction
capacity.
    When reagent completely reacts and solute solubility in the
membrane and internal phases is inconsequential, the globule capacity is 88.88. Table II compares this reaction-only number to the
total capacity including solute solubility. How closely condition
27 is satisfied will determine the size of the deviations in these
two numbers. When solubility does contribute, predictions of extractor performance based on the pseudosteady-state advancing front
approach will tend to be conservative. This underprediction of
extraction performance can be removed by including additional terms
in the perturbation solution described by Ho et al. (26). A simple
alternate procedure is described next.
    Figure 3 shows the fractional utilization of emulsion, F_e, as
a function of emulsion residence time for the same set of conditions as in Figure 2. To be consistent with the pseudosteady-state
solution of the advancing front theory, we have taken $(\sigma_4^i{}_{,max} -
\sigma_4^o)_{AF} = \sigma_2^+\sigma_3$ for the advancing front calculations. Calculations
made at flow rate ratios (v_b/v_e) of 9 and 19. Both models predict
that F_e is independent of the flow rate ratio and give the same
values when $(1+\sigma_4^o)/\sigma_4^o \approx 1$. Normalizing the pseudosteady-state
advancing front solution by the reagent capacity eliminates the
differences arising from solute solubility which were observed in
Figure 2. When $(1+\sigma_4^o)/\sigma_4^o$ deviates from 1, the reversible reaction
model predicts a faster emulsion utilization because the capacity
of the emulsion is much smaller, as already noted in Table II.
    Figure 4 demonstrates the effect of various concentrations of
internal phase reagent and bulk phase solute (σ_3 and σ_4^o) at fixed
ratios of σ_3/σ_4^o (2, 20, 200, and 2000). For this combination of

Table I. Example Concentration for Typical Solutes

Component	K (25°C)	C_{Ab}^o (for σ_4^o =1)	σ_4^o (for C_{Ab}^o =1 ppm)
Phenol	11,000	8.6 ppm	0.12
Aniline	39,450	2.4 ppm	0.42
o—cresol	6,300	17.0 ppm	0.06
m—nitrophenol	530,000	0.26 ppm	3.81

σ_3 = 2000 v_b/v_e = 9 f_m = 0.6 K_{bm} = 1.0

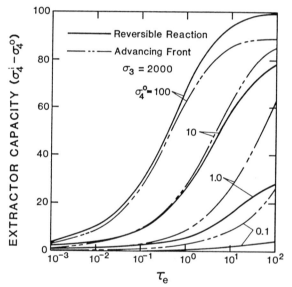

Figure 2 - Dimensionless extractor capacity as a function of τ_e (f_m=0.6, K_{mb}=1.0, v_b/v_e=9)

Table II. Maximum Globule Capacity, $(\sigma_{4,\ max}^i - \sigma_4^o)$

σ_4^o	Reversible Reaction Total	Advancing Front Total	Advancing Front Reaction Only
0.1	8.09	88.89	88.88
1.0	44.56	88.99	88.88
10	81.92	89.99	88.88
100	99.12	99.99	88.88

σ_3 = 2000 v_b/v_e = 9 f_m = 0.6 K_{bm} = 1.0

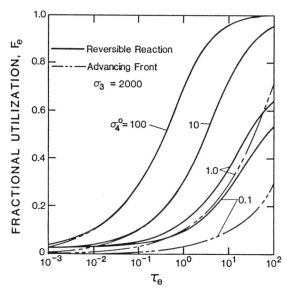

Figure 3 - Fractional utilization of emulsion globules as a function of τ_e. For $\sigma_4^0 > 10$ advancing front and reversible reaction predictions coincide ($f_m = 0.6$, $K_{mb} = 1.0$, $v_b/v_e = 9$ and 19).

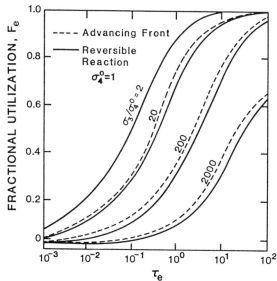

Figure 4 - Fractional utilization of emulsion globules as a function of τ_e at fixed σ_3/σ_4^0 ratios of 2, 20, 200 and 2000. For $\sigma_4^0 > 10$ advancing front and reversible reaction predictions coincide ($f_m = 0.6$, $K_{mb} = 1.0$, $v_b/v_e = 9$).

conditions, the effect of changing σ_4^0 from 1 to 100 is negligible when σ_3/σ_4^0 is 2.0 and small when σ_3/σ_4^0 is larger than 20.

For σ_4^0 equal to 10 or larger, the advancing front and reversible reaction models predict identical curves which depend only on the ratio of σ_3/σ_4^0. In this situation, extraction curves like those in Figure 2 can be developed by modifying the pseudosteady-state advancing front calculation slightly:

$$\left(\sigma_4^i - \sigma_4^0 \right) = \frac{\left(\sigma_{4,max}^i - \sigma_4^0 \right)_{RR}}{\sigma_2^+ \sigma_3} \int_0^1 \chi^2 \exp\left[- \frac{\sigma_2^+ \sigma_3 \left(1 - 3\chi^2 + 2\chi^3 \right)}{6 \sigma_1^+ \sigma_4^0 \tau_e} \right] d\chi \tag{39}$$

This is an appealing result since it obviates the numerical solution of the nonlinear partial differential equation.

The approach of Equation 39 is not generally successful when σ_4^0 is less than 10. As expected, the differences between the advancing front and reversible reaction predictions of F_e as a function of τ_e grow larger as σ_4^0 becomes smaller. Figure 5 illustrates this phenomenon for σ_3/σ_4^0 of 200. If the advancing front calculation is used as described in Equation 39, the design will always be conservative. For example, the residence time predicted by the advancing front for σ_4^0 of 0.1 and F_e of 0.5 is nearly one order of magnitude larger than that predicted by reversible reaction. However, when σ_4^0 is 0.1, $(1 + \sigma_4^0)$ is nearly equal to 1 and Equation 33 will apply. Consequently, simplified approaches for calculating extractor capacity exist except when σ_4^0 is neither large nor small (that is, both $(1 + \sigma_4^0)$ and $(1 + \sigma_4^0)/\sigma_4^0$ are not approximately 1). Next, we consider the case when neither of these two limiting conditions are met.

Differences between the advancing front and reversible reaction curves in Figures 4 and 5 arise because the advancing front theory assumes that all of the trapped reagent reacts. In fact, the reagent can only react until the equilibrium concentration of reagent is reached. One way to improve the advancing front prediction when σ_4^0 is small but $(1 + \sigma_4^0)$ is not close to 1 is to adjust the concentration of internal reagent (through the dimensionless parameter σ_3) to the amount which actually can react. The adjustment of σ_3 is determined by equating the amount of solute which is extracted by reaction for the advancing front and reversible reaction theories (see Equations 35 and 36) to obtain:

$$\sigma_{3,adj} = \frac{\sigma_3 \sigma_4^0}{1 + \sigma_4^0} \tag{40}$$

Table III shows values of $\sigma_{3,adj}$ for various σ_4^0 when the ratio σ_3/σ_4^0 is fixed at 200 and σ_1^+ and σ_2^+ are 0.0667 and 0.0444, respectively.

When σ_4^0 becomes small, the contribution of reaction to the extraction decreases and extraction by phase solubility becomes proportionally more important. The right hand column in Table III gives the fraction of total extracted solute which would be removed by reaction only.

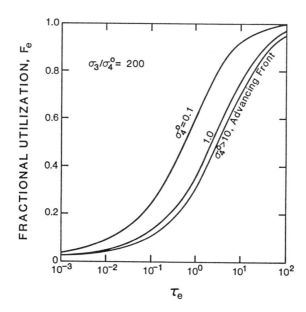

Figure 5 - Fractional utilization of emulsion globules as a function of τ_e for σ_3/σ_4^0 of 200 and σ_4^0 of 0.1, 1.0, 10 and larger. For $\sigma_4^0 > 10$ advancing front and reversible reaction predictions coincide ($f_m = 0.6$, $K_{mb} = 1.0$, $v_b/v_e = 9$)

Table III. Adjusted Reagent Concentration and Fraction of Solute Extracted by Reaction with Reagent

σ_4^0	σ_3	$\sigma_{3,adj}$	$\dfrac{\sigma_2\sigma_{3,adj}}{\sigma_4^0(\sigma_1^+ + \sigma_2^+) + \sigma_2^+\sigma_{3,adj}}$
10	2000	1818	0.986
1	200	100	0.976
0.5	100	33.3	0.964
0.1	20	1.818	0.879
0.01	0.2	0.00198	0.073

$\sigma_3/\sigma_4^0 = 200$ $\sigma_1 = 0.0667$ $\sigma_2 = 0.0444$

Accordingly, membrane and internal phase solubility and the effect on extraction rate can be incorporated into advancing front estimates of fractional utilization,

$$F_{e,adj} = \frac{(\sigma_4^i - \sigma_4^0)_{adj}}{\sigma_2^+ \ \sigma_{3,adj}} \tag{41}$$

where $(\sigma_4^i - \sigma_4^0)_{adj}$ is calculated using $\sigma_{3,adj}$ in the pseudosteady-state solution of the advancing front theory. Equation 41, which is consistent with the pseudosteady-state assumption in Equation 27, assumes extraction is by reaction only.

Figures 6-8 compare adjusted and nonadjusted advancing front predictions with the small σ_4^0 approximation and the numerically-solved reversible reaction model for σ_3/σ_4^0 of 200 and σ_4^0 values of 1.0, 0.5 and 0.1. The nonadjusted advancing front curve is the same in all three plots, because the advancing front solution depends only on the ratio σ_3/σ_4^0, which is fixed. When σ_4^0 is 0.1, differences between the small σ_4^0 and reversible reaction curves are small and within the error of the numerical solution. As expected, the small σ_4^0 approximation is poor when σ_4^0 is 1 and the condition that $(1 + \sigma_4^0) \approx 1$ no longer applies. In this situation, the adjusted advancing front approach can be used to estimate reasonable design parameters. For σ_4^0 of 0.5, the adjusted advancing front and small σ_4^0 predictions bracket the reversible reaction solution.

Conclusions

Small solute concentrations in the extractor may not be sufficient to force all the reagent in the emulsion globules to react. Design calculations which include this dependence on solute concentrations have been developed. Comparison with the pseudosteady-state advancing front approach showed significant differences which would lead to overdesign when σ_4^0 is large and to underdesign when σ_4^0 is small.

Three methods which do not require solution of the nonlinear partial differential equation are presented for estimating extractor performance. The choice of method depends on the value of the dimensionless outlet solute concentration, σ_4^0. If $(\sigma_4^0 + 1)/\sigma_4^0$ is close to 1, the reaction is effectively irreversible and the pseudosteady-state solution of the advancing front model satisfactorily predicts performance after normalization to include solute solubility in the globule. If $(\sigma_4^0 + 1)/\sigma_4^0$ is not close to 1, the advancing front results will still apply, provided that the amount of solute extracted by reaction is small and membrane solubility controls. When σ_4^0 is small enough so that $(\sigma_4^0 + 1)$ is close to 1, then the reversible reaction model can be reduced to a linear equation with an analytical solution. Otherwise, for σ_4^0 values when neither $(\sigma_4^0 + 1)$ nor $(\sigma_4^0 + 1)/\sigma_4$ is nearly 1, a reasonable first approximation is made by adjusting the actual concentration of internal reagent to an effective concentration which equals the amount consumed to reach equilibrium.

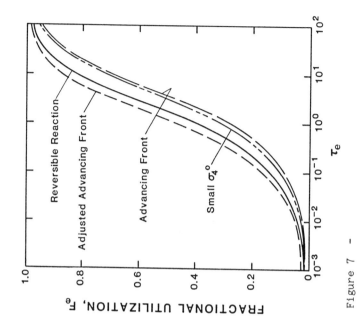

Figure 7 –

Comparison of reversible reaction, small σ_4^o approximation, and adjusted and nonadjusted advancing front calculation of fractional utilization as a function of τ_e for σ_3/σ_4^o of 200 and σ_4^o of 0.5 ($f_m=0.6$, $K_{mb}=1.0$, $v_b/v_e=9$).

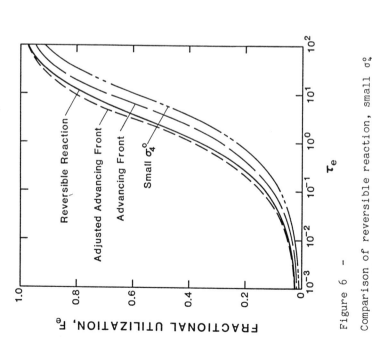

Figure 6 –

Comparison of reversible reaction, small σ_4^o approximation, and adjusted and nonadjusted advancing front calculations of fractional utilization as a function of τ_e for σ_3/σ_4^o of 200 and σ_4^o of 1.0 ($f_m=0.6$, $K_{mb}=1.0$, $v_b/v_e=9$).

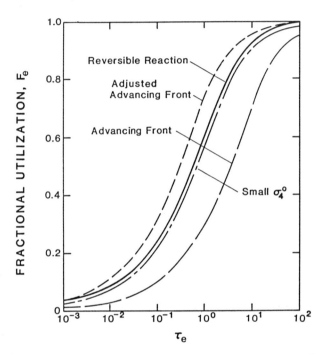

Figure 8 - Comparison of reversible reaction, small σ_4^0
            approximation, and adjusted and nonadjusted
            advancing front calculations of fractional
            utilization as a function of τ_e for σ_3/σ_4^0 of 200
            and σ_4^0 of 0.1 ($f_m=0.6$, $K_{mb}=1.0$, $v_b/v_e=9$).

Acknowledgments

        This work was supported in part by the Environmental Protec-
tion Agency (Grant No. R811247-01-0) and the National Bureau of
Standards (Coop Agreement NB83RAH 30001). The assistance of Mr.
Paul Nornes was greatly appreciated.

Legend of Symbols

C_{Ab}	Bulk phase solute concentration, M
C_{Ai}	Internal phase solute concentration, M
C_{Am}	Membrane phase solute concentration, M
C_{Bi}	Internal phase reagent concentration, M
C_{Pi}	Internal phase product concentration, M
D_{eff}	Effective solute diffusivity in the emulsion globule based on the membrane driving force and including concentration-dependent reaction effects, m^2/s
$\overline{D}_{eff}$	Mean effective solute diffusivity in the emulsion globule based on the membrane phase driving force and including reaction effects, m^2/s
D	Solute diffusion coefficient, m^2/s
f_m	Membrane volume fraction of the emulsion
F_e	Fractional utilization of emulsion
K	Reaction equilibrium constant, M^{-1}
K_{mb}	Partition coefficient between the membrane and continuous bulk phases
K_{mi}	Partition coefficient between the membrane and internal phases
$\dot{m}_A$	Overall solute mass transfer rate
M	Molarity, mol/dm^3
N_T	Total number of globules in the extractor
$n(t)$	Number of globules having having a residence greater than t
r	Radial coordinate, cm
R	Global radius, cm
t	Time, s
t_e	Emulsion residence time, V_e/v_e, s
v	Volumetric flowrate, dm^3/s
V	Phase volume, dm^3

Greek Letters

γ	Diffusion, enhancement factor
η	Normalized radial coordinate
λ	Ratio of reaction-effected diffusion coefficient to the no reaction diffusion coefficient
σ_1	Dimensionless parameter
σ_2	Dimensionless parameter
σ_3	Dimensionless reagent concentration
σ_4	Dimensionless solute concentration
τ	Dimensionless time
ϕ	Normalized solute concentration
χ	Dimensionless reaction front position

82

LIQUID MEMBRANES: THEORY AND APPLICATIONS

Subscripts

A	Solute
adj	Adjusted
B	Reagent
b	Continuous bulk phase
e	Emulsion
i	Internal phase
max	Maximum
m	Membrane phase
NR	No reaction
P	Reaction product
r	Reference
R	Reaction

Superscripts

f	Feed
i	Initial or inlet
o	Outlet
+	Continuous extraction definition

Literature Cited

1. Schiffer, D.K.; Hochhauser, A.; Evans, D.F.; Cussler, E.L. Nature, 1974, 250, 484.
2. Hochhauser, A.M.; Cussler, E.L. AIChE Symp. Ser., 1975, 71, 136.
3. Martin, T.P.; Davies, G.A. Hydrometallurgy, 1976/1977, 2, 315.
4. Kondo, K.; Kita, K.; Koida, I.; Irie, J.; Nakashio, F. J. Chem. Eng. Japan, 1979, 12, 203.
5. Kondo, K.; Kita, K.; Nakashio, F. J. Chem. Eng. Japan, 1981, 14, 20.
6. Völkel, W.; Halwachs, W.; Schugerl, K. J. Membrane Sci., 1980, 6, 19.
7. Strezelbicki, J.; Charewicz, W. Hydrometallurgy, 1980, 5, 243.
8. Schlosser, S.; Kossackzy, E. J. Membrane Sci., 1980, 6, 83.
9. Frankenfeld, J.W.; Cahn, R.P.; Li, N.N. Sep. Sci. Tech., 1981, 16, 385.
10. Boch, J.; Valint, P.L. Ind. Eng. Chem. Fund., 1982, 21, 417.
11. Hayworth, H.C.; Ho, W.S.; Burns, W.A.; Li, N.N. AIChE Nat. Meeting, No. 56d, Orlando, FL, 1982.
12. Teramoto, M.; Sakai, T.; Yanagawa, K.; Ohsuga, M.; Miyake, Y. Sep. Sci. Tech., 1983, 18, 735.
13. Li, N.N. AIChE, J., 1971, 17, 459.
14. Li, N.N. Ind. Eng. Chem. Process Des. Dev., 1971, 10, 215.
15. Shah, N.D.; Owens, T.C. Ind. Eng. Chem. Prod. Res. Dev., 1972, 11, 58.
16. Kremesec, V.J.; Slattery, J.C. AIChE J., 1982, 28, 492.
17. Cahn, R.P.; Li, N.N. Sep. Sci., 1974, 9, 505.

18. Cahn, R.P.; Li, N.N.; Minday, R.M. Environ. Sci. Tech., 1978, 12, 1051.
19. Li, N.N.; Shrier, A.L. In Recent Development in Separation Science; Li, N.N., Ed.; No. 1; Chemical Rubber Company: Cleveland, OH, 1972; p 163.
20. Frankenfeld, J.W.; Li, N.N. In Recent Developments in Separation Science; Li, N.N., Ed.; No. 3; Chemical Rubber Company: Cleveland, OH, 1977; p 285.
21. Kitagawa, T.; Nishikawa, Y.; Frankenfeld, J.W.; Li, N.N. Environ. Sci. Technol., 1977, 11, 602.
22. Halwachs, W.; Flaschel, E.; Schügerl, K. J. Membrane Sci., 1980, 6, 33.
23. Terry, R.E.; Li, N.N., Ho, W.S.; J. Membrane Sci., 1982, 10, 305.
24. Teramoto, M.; Takihana, H.; Shibutani, M.; Yuasa, T.; Miyake, Y.; Teranishi, H. J. Chem. Eng. Japan, 1981, 14, 122.
25. Teramoto, M.; Takihana, H.; Shibutani, M.; Yuasa, T.; Hara, N. Sep. Sci. Tech., 1983, 18, 397.
26. Ho, W.S.; Hatton, T.A.; Lightfoot, E.N.; Li, N.N. AIChE J., 1982, 28, 662.
27. Hatton, T.A.; Lightfoot, E.N.; Cahn, R.P.; Li, N.N. Ind. Eng. Chem. Fund., 1983, 22, 27.
28. May, S.W.; Li, N.N. Biochem. Biophy. Res. Commun., 1972, 47, 1179.
29. May, S.W.; Li, N.N. In Enzyme Engineering; Pye, E.K.; Wingaard, L.B., Eds.; No.1; Plenum Press: New York, 1974; p 77.
30. May, S.W.; Li, N.N. In Biomed. Appl. of Immobilized Enzymes and Proteins; Chang, T.M.S., Ed.; No. 1; Plenum Press: New York, 1977; p 171.
31. Li, N.N.; Asher, W.J. In Chemical Engineering in Medicine; Reneau, D.D., Ed.; Advances in Chemistry Series No. 118; American Chemical Society: Washington, DC, 1973; p 1.
32. Mohan, R.R.; Li, N.N. Biotechnol. Bioeng., 1974, 16, 513.
33. Mohan, R.R.; Li, N.N. Biotechnol. Bioeng., 1975, 17, 1137.
34. Asher, W.J.; Bovee, K.C.; Frankenfeld, J.W.; Hamilton, R.W.; Henderson, L.W.; Holtzapple, P.G.; Li, N.N. Kidney Int. Suppl., 1975, 3, 409.
35. Asher, W.J.; Vogler, T.C.; Bovee, K.C.; Holtzapple, P.G.; Hamilton, R.W. Trans. Am. Soc. Artif. Intern. Organs, 1977, 23, 673.
36. Frankenfeld, J.W.; Asher, W.J.; Li, N.N. In Recent Developments in Separation Science; Li, N.N., Ed.; No. 4; Chemical Rubber Company: Cleveland, Ohio, 1978; p 39.
37. Hatton, T.A.; Wardius, D.S. AIChE J., 1984, 30, 934.
38. Wardius, D.S.; Hatton, T.A. Chem. Eng. Comm., 1985, 37, 159.
39. Bunge, A.L.; Noble, R.D. J. Membrane Sci., 1984, 21, 55.
40. Baird, R.S.; Bunge, A.L.; Noble, R.D. AIChE J., 1987, 33, 43.
41. Baird, R.S. M.S. Thesis, Colorado School of Mines, Golden, Colorado, 1985.
42. Crank, J. The Mathematics of Diffusion, 2nd Ed., Clarendon Press: Oxford, England, 1975; p 274.
43. Jefferson, T.B.; Witzell, O.W.; Sibbet, W.L. Ind. Eng. Chem., 1958, 50, 1589.

RECEIVED March 31, 1987

CARRIER CHEMISTRY

Chapter 6

Proton-Coupled Transport of Alkali Metal Cations Across Liquid Membranes by Ionizable Crown Ethers

Richard A. Bartsch, Witold A. Charewicz[1], Sang Ihn Kang, and Wladyslaw Walkowiak[1]

Department of Chemistry and Biochemistry, Texas Tech University, Lubbock, TX 79409-4260

Crown ether carboxylic acids and phosphonic acid mono-alkyl esters are novel reagents for the active transport of alkali metal cations across organic liquid membranes. Metal ion transport is coupled to the back transport of protons. The influence of structural variation within the ionizable crown ether carrier molecule upon the selectivity and efficiency of competitive alkali metal transport across bulk liquid, liquid surfactant (emulsion) and polymer-supported liquid membranes is assessed.

Transport of ionic species through liquid membranes is of central importance in biological systems and is playing an increasing role in the development of practical separation schemes. Of the several transport mechanisms which have been demonstrated, coupled transport mediated by mobile carriers (ionophores) is one of the simplest mechanisms for the selective removal of a desired ion from a dilute solution. In such a system, the flux of one ion moving down its concentration gradient may be used to drive the transport of the desired cation up its concentration gradient. In such active transport, a pH gradient with back transport of protons is used most often to drive the transport of another cationic species from basic to acidic solution. Metal ion transport coupled with back transport of protons has been demonstrated in natural and artificial systems for many of the carboxylate ionophore antibiotics. Thus, Na^+ was pumped from basic to acidic solution through a supported octanol membrane which contained the sodium-specific antibiotic monensin (1). Similarly Ca^{2+} is transported across bulk liquid membranes and from vesicles by lascaloid (X 537-A) and calcimycin (A 23187) (2-5).

---

[1]Present address: Institute of Inorganic Chemistry and Metallurgy of the Rare Elements, Technical University of Wroclaw, 50370 Wroclaw, Poland

Due to their pronounced selectivity in metal ion complexation (6), crown ethers (macrocyclic polyethers) and related macrocyclic multidentate ligands are attractive mobile carriers for metal ion transport across liquid membranes. As summarized in recent reviews of macrocycle-facilitated transport of ions in liquid membrane systems (7,8), most studies have been conducted with macrocyclic carriers which do not possess ionizable groups. For such carriers, metal ions can only be transported down their concentration gradients unless some type of auxiliary complexing agent is present in the receiving aqueous phase.

To take advantage of the attractive features of proton-coupled transport, we (9-12) and others (14-17) have utilized crown ether compounds with pendant carboxylic acid groups. The mechanism of proton-coupled transport of a monovalent metal cation across an organic liquid membrane is illustrated in Figure 1. Thus the carrier, which remains in the organic membrane, is deprotonated at the organic phase-alkaline aqueous source phase interface and complexes the metal cation (Step 1). The electroneutral complex then diffuses across the organic membrane (Step 2). At the organic phase-acidic aqueous receiving phase interface, the carboxylate group of the carrier is protonated which releases the metal cation into the receiving phase (Step 3). The carrier molecule then diffuses back across the organic membrane (Step 4) to begin another cycle. Thus metal ion transport from the source to the receiving aqueous phase is coupled to proton transport from the receiving to the source aqueous phase. It should be noted that for such crown ether carboxylic acid carriers, concomitant transport of the metal ion and an anion from the aqueous source phase is not required. (As is the case for crown ethers without ionizable groups). This factor is of immense importance for potential practical applications of macrocycle-facilitated transport processes since such systems would most probably involve such poorly-transportable source phase anions as chloride, nitrate and sulfate (18).

In the present paper, we examine the influence of structural variation within series of crown ether carboxylic acid and crown ether phosphonic acid monoalkyl ester carriers upon the selectivity and efficiency of alkali metal transport across three types of liquid organic membranes. Structural variations within the carriers include the polyether ring size, the lipophilic group attachment site and the basicity of ethereal oxygens. The three membrane types are bulk liquid membranes, liquid surfactant (emulsion) membranes and polymer-supported liquid membranes.

Ionizable Crown Ethers

The ionizable crown ethers which were utilized in the metal ion transport studies include a series of dibenzo crown ether carboxylic acids 1-6 and a series of crown ether phosphonic acid monoethyl esters 7-10 (Figure 2). Within the first series, the crown ether ring size is systematically varied from 14-crown-4 to 16-crown-5 to 19-crown-6 in compounds 1, 2 and 3, respectively. For compounds 2, 4 and 5, the crown ether ring size is held constant but the attachment site of the lipophilic alkyl group is altered. Finally, for compounds 2 and 6, the crown ether ring size and lipophilic

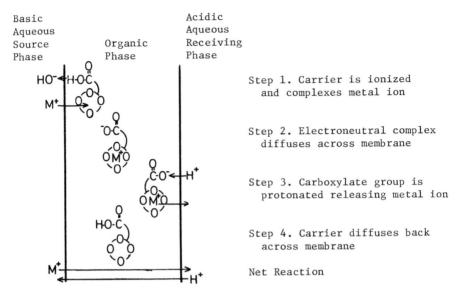

Basic Aqueous Source Phase	Organic Phase	Acidic Aqueous Receiving Phase	

Step 1. Carrier is ionized and complexes metal ion

Step 2. Electroneutral complex diffuses across membrane

Step 3. Carboxylate group is protonated releasing metal ion

Step 4. Carrier diffuses back across membrane

Net Reaction

Figure 1.   Mechanism of Proton-coupled Metal Ion Transport by an Ionizable Crown Ether.

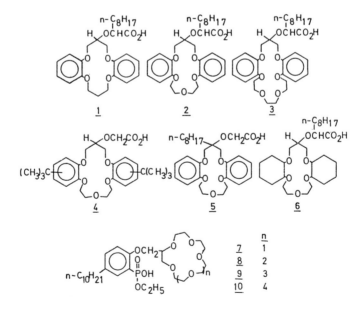

Figure 2.   Structures of Ionizable Crown Ethers.

group attachment site are maintained, but the basicity of several ethereal oxygens is changed when four aryl alkyl ether oxygen atoms are converted into more basic dialkyl ether oxygens. In the second series which involves a more acidic ionizable function, the structural variation is a systematic increase in crown ether ring size from 15-crown-5 to 18-crown-6 to 21-crown-7 to 24-crown-8 in compounds 7, 8, 9 and 10, respectively.

Polyether cavity diameters for these crown ethers as estimated from Corey-Pauling-Kortum (CPK) space-filling models or determined from X-ray crystal data are compared with the alkali metal cation diameters in Table I (6,13). In general, strongest complexation is expected when the ratio of metal ion to polyether cavity diameters

Table I. Comparison of Polyether Cavity and Cation Diameters

Cation	Diameter (Å)	Crown Ether	Diameter Å
Li^+	1.48	14-Crown-4	1.2-1.5
Na^+	2.04	15-Crown-5	1.72-1.85
K^+	2.76	16-Crown-5	2.0-2.4
Rb^+	2.98	18-Crown-6	2.68-2.86
Cs^+	3.40	19-Crown-6	3.0-3.5
		21-Crown-7	3.4
		24-Crown-8	4.0

is 0.8-0.9 (19). If complexation is the determining factor in transport, then selectivity in alkali metal cation transport should be strongly influenced by the cavity size of the macrocyclic carrier molecule.

Transport of Alkali Metal Cations Across Bulk Liquid Membranes

Our initial investigation (9) of alkali metal cation transport involved bulk chloroform membranes and the simple U-tube apparatus shown in Figure 3. The aqueous source phase A was a solution of an alkali metal chloride and hydroxide which was maintained at pH = 9. Organic phase B was a solution of a crown ether carboxylic acid in chloroform. Receiving aqueous phase C was 0.1 N HCl. Using this apparatus, transport by crown ether carboxylic acid 2 from source phases which contained single alkali metal cation species was first performed. Then transport behavior was examined for a source phase in which all five alkali metal cations were present. Results from the five single species transport experiments are superimposed on a common plot and presented in Figure 4a. The single species results suggested a transport selectivity of $Na^+, K^+ > Rb^+ > Li^+, Cs^+$. Surprisingly different results were obtained from the competitive transport experiment (Figure 4b). Thus in competitive transport of all five alkali metal cations by crown ether carboxylic acid 2, the selectivity was $Na^+ >> K^+ > Li^+, Rb^+, Cs^+$. These results underscore the dangers of extrapolating anticipated competitive transport behavior

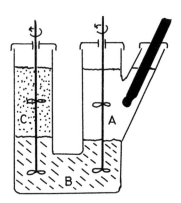

Figure 3. U-Tube Apparatus for Bulk Liquid Membrane Transport Experiments (A = alkaline aqueous source phase, B = chloroform phase containing carrier, C = acidic aqueous receiving phase, phases stirred at 200 rpm, pH electrode shown in black).

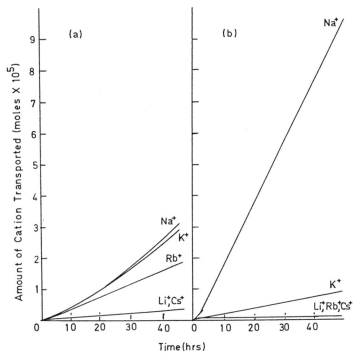

Figure 4. Transport of Alkali Metal Cations Across a Bulk Chloroform Membrane (a = single species transport, b = competitive transport). (Adapted with permission from Ref. 9. Copyright 1982 Elsevier.)

from single species measurements. For this reason, our subsequent investigations have utilized only competitive transport experiments.

For later studies, a second generation transport cell (Figure 5) was employed. In this tube-within-a-beaker design, alkali metal cations are transported from the alkaline aqueous source phase A through the chloroform organic phase B which contains the ionizable crown ether and into the acidic aqueous receiving phase C. Transport selectivities for crown ether carboxylic acid carriers 1, 2 and 3 were: $Na^+>K^+>Li^+,Rb^+,Cs^+$; $Na^+>>K^+>Li^+,Rb^+,Cs^+$; and $K^+>Rb^+>Na^+>Li^+,Cs^+$; respectively. Thus, high Na^+ transport selectivity was again observed for the 16-crown-5 carrier 2. Although the 14-crown-4 ring in 1 would be expected to favor interactions with Li^+, transport of Na^+ was favored. On the other hand, with 3 selectivity for K^+ transport was observed as would be anticipated for the 19-crown-6 ring size.

The influence of lipophilic group attachment site variation was examined for competitive alkali metal cation transport through the chloroform membrane by the series of isomeric crown ether carboxylic acids 2, 4 and 5. All three carriers exhibited the transport selectivity of $Na^+>>K^+>Li^+,Rb^+,Cs^+$ and for 5, which showed the highest selectivity, only Na^+ and K^+ could be detected in the receiving phase. Examination of CPK models reveals that the carboxylic acid group is located directly over the crown ether ring in 5 when the lipophilic tail is pointed directly away from the polar polyether portion of the carrier molecule. Apparently such pre-organization of the binding site produces enhanced selectivity.

For the pair of ionizable crown ethers 2 and 6, the structural modification is to replace four alkyl aryl ether oxygens with more electron-rich dialkyl ether oxygens. The transport selectivity of $Na^+>>K^+>Li^+,Rb^+,Cs^+$ was the same for both carriers which indicates that the variation of oxygen basicity has little influence upon bulk liquid membrane transport behavior for this compound series.

The structural variation of crown ether ring size charge was examined in more detail with the crown ether phosphonic acid monoethyl ester series 7-10 for which the crown ether ring size is systematically varied from 15-crown-5 to 18-crown-6 to 21-crown-7 to 24-crown-8. As shown in Figure 6, 7 and 8 exhibit transport selectivity for Na^+ and K^+ as would be predicted for their ring sizes. Similarly for 9, which has a larger 21-crown-7 ring, transport selectivity for the larger alkali metal cations Rb^+ and Cs^+ is observed. However when the crown ether ring size is expanded even further to 24-crown-8, very unselective transport was observed in which all of the alkali metal cations except Li^+ passed through the chloroform membrane with equal efficiency. Such loss of transport selectivity suggests that for 10 the large polyether ring does not remain planar but distorts to provide a more three-dimensional type of complexation which accommodates a variety of cation sizes.

The results provided above demonstrate that considerable selectivity can be achieved in alkali metal transport across bulk chloroform membranes by appropriately-structured ionizable crown ether carrier molecules. Although such bulk liquid membrane transport studies provide valuable information concerning the selectivity of alkali metal cation transport, the actual amount of

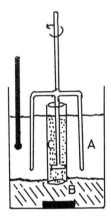

Figure 5. Cell for Bulk Liquid Membrane Transport Experiments (A = alkaline aqueous source phase, B = chloroform phase containing carrier, C = acidic aqueous receiving phase, phases A and C stirred at 120 rpm, phase B stirred with 200 rpm stirring bar, pH electrode shown in black). (Adapted from Ref. 10. Copyright 1982 American Chemical Society.)

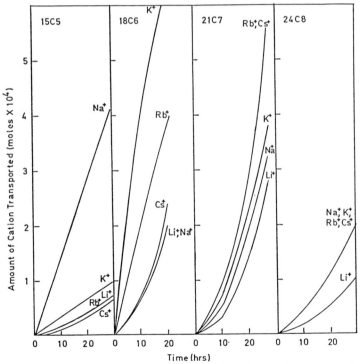

Figure 6. Competitive Transport of Alkali Metal Cations Across Bulk Chloroform Membranes by Crown Ether Phosphonic Acid Monoethyl Esters 7-10.

cations which cross into the receiving phase is quite low due to the thickness of the liquid membrane. Greater potential for the development of practical separation schemes lies in the areas of liquid surfactant (emulsion) membranes and polymer-supported liquid membranes.

Transport of Alkali Metal Cation Across Liquid Surfactant (Emulsion) Membranes

The principle of the liquid surfactant membrane technique which was developed by Li and Shrier (20) is based on the separation of internal (receiving phase) and external (source phase) aqueous solutions by an organic liquid membrane in a water-in-oil-in-water (W/O/W) type emulsion. Such emulsions are prepared by an initial rapid blending of an aqueous solution (which will become the internal aqueous phase) with an oil phase in the presence of an emulsifying agent to form a water-in-oil (W/O) emulsion and then by adding this emulsion to an aqueous solution which is the external aqueous phase. The organic liquid membrane is a water-immiscible phase which contains the emulsifying agent (surfactant) and the carrier species in a hydrocarbon solvent.

An idealized schematic diagram of alkali metal cation transport across a liquid surfactant (emulsion) membrane by an ionizable crown ether is shown in Figure 7. Thus a metal cation is transported from an external aqueous source phase across the liquid surfactant membrane which forms the outer surface of the emulsion droplet into an interior aqueous receiving phase. Metal ion transport is driven by a pH gradient and back transport of protons from the internal to the external aqueous solution according to the mechanism illustrated earlier in Figure 1. In this system, transport is rapid due to the thin organic membrane.

For our studies (13), the organic liquid membrane was a solution of the ionizable crown ether carrier in a mixture of mineral oil (50%), toluene (45%), and 5% of Span 80 (sorbitan monooleate). The external (source) aqueous phase contained LiCl, NaCl, KCl, and RbCl and was maintained at pH 8.5 by addition of concentrated CsOH solution. The internal (receiving) aqueous phase was 0.2 M HCl.

The influence of polyether ring size upon the competitive transport of four alkali metal cations by crown ether carboxylic acids 1-3 (13) is shown in Figure 8. Curvature of the plots results from depletion of acid from the internal aqueous solution by back transport of protons. Although Li^+ transport selectivity was not observed with the 14-crown-4 carrier 1, modest Na^+ transport selectivity by 2 and pronounced K^+ transport selectivity by 3 was achieved. The selectivities for alkali metal transport across liquid surfactant membranes by crown ether carboxylic acids 1-3 were very similar to those noted in the bulk liquid membrane experiments. However, transport is now complete in a matter of minutes rather than hours.

A marked influence of lipophilic group attachment site variation upon transport selectivity and efficiency (13) is shown in Figure 9. Thus for the isomeric crown ether carboxylic acid carriers 2, 4 and 5, both the selectivity for Na^+ transport and the

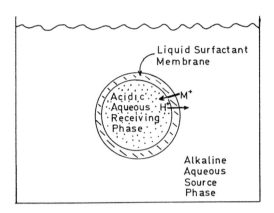

Figure 7. Schematic Diagram of Proton-coupled Transport Across a Liquid Surfactant (Emulsion) Membrane.

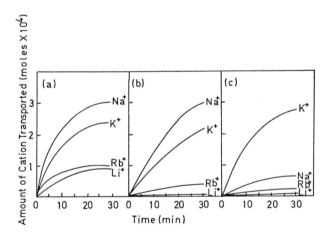

Figure 8. Influence of Polyether Ring Size Upon Competitive Transport of Alkali Metal Cations Across a Liquid Surfactant Membrane by (a) 1, (b) 2, and (c) 3. (Adapted with permission from Ref. 13. Copyright 1984 Elsevier.)

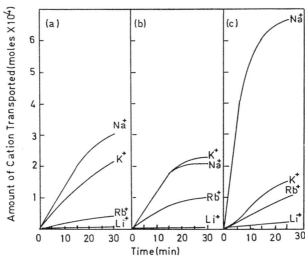

Figure 9. Influence of Lipophilic Group Attachment Site Upon Competitive Transport of Alkali Metal Cations Across a Liquid Surfactant Membrane by (a) 2, (b) 4, and (c) 5. (Adapted with permission from Ref. 13. Copyright 1984 Elsevier.)

overall transport efficiency were highest with 5 for which the ionizable group may be positioned directly over the polyether cavity (vide supra).

For both crown ether carboxylic acid carriers 2 and 6, the transport selectivities are $Na^+>K^+>Rb^+>Li^+$. Somewhat higher selectivity for Na^+ transport and transport efficiency were noted for 6 which has the more basic ether oxygens (13).

Results from these experiments demonstrate that alkali metal cation separations can be achieved on an attractive time scale using ionizable crown ethers in liquid surfactant membrane systems.

Transport of Alkali Metal Cations Across Polymer-Supported Liquid Membranes

An alternative method for producing thin liquid membranes is to separate the source and receiving aqueous phases with an organic liquid which is held within the pores of an inert porous polymer.

Results of our initial studies of alkali metal cation transport across such a polymer-supported liquid membrane by ionizable crown ethers are most encouraging. In our system, the source phase was a solution of $NaHCO_3$, KCl and RbCl (each 0.10 M) and the receiving phase was aqueous HCl (0.50 M). These solutions were separated by a flat Accurel polypropylene membrane (from Enka) loaded with a 0.01 M o-nitrophenyl octyl ether solution of an analog of 5 in which the n-octyl group was replaced by a n-decyl group. The aqueous solutions were stirred slowly at 200 rpm. Concentrations of alkali metal cations in the receiving phase as a function of time are shown in Figure 10. For this carrier, which is anticipated to be selective for Na^+ transport, only Na^+ was detected in the receiving phase. Such striking selectivity in this polymer-supported liquid membrane system most assuredly warrants further investigation.

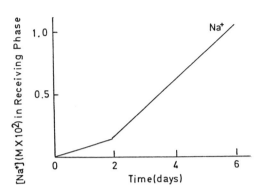

Figure 10. Competitive Alkali Metal Transport Across a Polymer-supported Liquid Membrane by an Analog of 5.

Conclusions

Ionizable crown ethers are effective agents for the proton-coupled transport of alkali metal cations across bulk liquid, liquid surfactant, and polymer-supported liquid membranes. The selectivity and efficiency of competitive alkali metal cation transport can be controlled by structural variation within the ionizable crown ether carrier. Such systems possess considerable potential for practical separations of specified alkali metal cations from aqueous solutions.

Acknowledgment

This research was supported by the Office of Basic Energy Sciences of the United States Department of Energy (Contract DE-AS05-80ER-10604).

Literature Cited

1. Chow, E. M.; Evans, D. F.; Cussler, E. L. J. Am. Chem. Soc. 1974, 96, 7085-7090.
2. Pressman, B. C.; Guzman, N. T. Ann. N. Y. Acad. Sci. 1975, 264, 373-386.
3. Malaisse, W. J.; Valverde, I.; Devis, G.; Somers, G.; Couturier, E. Biochimie 1979, 61, 1185-1192.
4. Couturier, E.; Malaisse, W. J. Biochimie 1980, 62, 177-180.
5. Bolte, J.; Demuynck, C.; Jeminet, G.; Juillard, J.; Tissier, C. Can. J. Chem. 1982, 60, 981-989.
6. Lamb, J. D.; Izatt, R. M.; Christensen, J. J. In Progress in Macrocyclic Chemistry; Izatt, R. M.; Christensen, J. J., Eds.; John Wiley and Sons: New York, 1981; Vol. 2, Chapter 2.
7. McBride, D. W., Jr.; Izatt, R. M.; Lamb, J. D.; Christensen, J. J. In Inclusion Compounds; Atwood, J. L.; Davies, J. E. D.; MacNicol, D. D., Eds.; Academic Press: New York, 1984; Chapter 16.

8. Izatt, R. M.; Clark, G. A.; Bradshaw, J. S.; Lamb, J. D.; Christensen, J. J. Sep. Purif. Methods 1986, 15, 21-72.
9. Strzelbicki, J.; Bartsch, R. A. J. Membrane Sci. 1982, 10, 35-47.
10. Charewicz, W. A.; Heo, G. S.; Bartsch, R. A. Anal. Chem. 1982, 54, 2094-2097.
11. Charewicz, W. A.; Bartsch, R. A. Anal. Chem. 1982, 54, 2300-2303.
12. Charewicz, W. A.; Bartsch, R. A. J. Membrane Sci. 1983, 12, 323-333.
13. Bartsch, R. A.; Charewicz, W. A., Kang, S. I. J. Membrane Sci. 1984, 17, 97-107.
14. Frederick, L. A.; Fyles, T. M.; Malik-Diemer, V. A.; Whitfield, D. M. J. Chem. Soc., Chem. Commun. 1980, 1211-1212.
15. Frederick, L. A.; Fyles, T. M.; Gurprasad, N. P.; Whitfield, D. M. Can. J. Chem. 1981, 59, 1724-1733.
16. Fyles, T. M.; Malik-Diemer, V. A.; Whitfield, D. M.; Can. J. Chem. 1981, 59, 1734-1744.
17. Fyles, T. M.; Malik-Diemer, V. A.; McGavin, C. A.; Whitfield, D. M. Can. J. Chem. 1982, 60, 2259-2267.
18. Lamb, J. D.; Christensen, J. J.; Izatt, S. R.; Bedke, K.; Astin, M. S.; Izatt, R. M. J. Am. Chem. Soc. 1980, 102, 3399-3403.
19. Christensen, J. J.; Hill, J. O.; Izatt, R. M. Science 1971, 174, 459-467.
20. Li, N. N.; Shrier, A. L. In Recent Developments in Separation Science; Li, N. N., Ed.; CRC Press: Cleveland, Ohio, 1972; Vol. 1, pp 163-174.

RECEIVED January 9, 1987

Chapter 7

Use of Coanion Type and Concentration in Macrocycle-Facilitated Metal Cation Separations with Emulsion Liquid Membranes

R. M. Izatt, R. L. Bruening, and J. J. Christensen

Departments of Chemistry and Chemical Engineering, Brigham Young University, Provo, UT 84602

Co-anion type and concentration are examined as parameters that can be varied to achieve various metal cation separations in macrocycle-facilitated emulsion liquid membranes. Membrane systems where the metal is present in the source phase as a complex anion or as a neutral complex (cation-anion(s)) are discussed. The experimental separations of Cd(II) from Zn(II) and/or Hg(II), Au(I) from Ag(I), and Au(III) from Pd(II) or Ag(I) are given to illustrate separation design using these membrane systems. The separations are discussed in terms of free energies of hydration, distribution coefficients, and equilibrium constants for the various interactions that occur.

A great deal of research in recent years has examined methods to separate and recover metal cations from waste streams and leached ore deposits. The limited amount of natural resources and the toxicity of some metals provide compelling reasons for this research. One method under study is the use of macrocycles as cation carriers in liquid membrane systems(1-6). The emulsion liquid membrane (ELM) has been particularly effective in macrocycle-mediated metal cation separation experiments.

The ELM was first introduced by Li in 1968(7). A typical water-oil-water ELM is illustrated in Figure 1. The ELM is superior to other artifical membranes in that 1) there is a large surface area at both aqueous-oil interfaces which enhances macrocycle-cation interaction and, hence, the rate of cation transport; 2) the transported cation is concentrated since the volume of the receiving phase is smaller than that of the source phase; and 3) emulsions can be made stable for long time periods (Izatt, R. M.; Bruening, R. L.; Cho, M. H.; Wu, G.; Lamb, J. D.; Christensen, J. J. J. Membr. Sci., submitted). The main disadvantages of the ELM are 1) the need to break down the emulsion after transport has occurred to recover the metal from the receiving phase and to recycle the macrocycle-containing organic phase; and 2) the co-transport of H_2O in some cases.

Macrocycles are effective carrier molecules in membranes for metal separations since they often selectively interact with a particular cation in a family of elements. Furthermore, lipophilic side chains can often be attached to the macrocycle ring without significantly altering the interactive properties of the macrocycle(8), but enhancing the distribution to the organic phase over the aqueous phase of both the macrocycle and the macrocycle-cation complex(Izatt, R. M.; Bruening, R. L.; Clark, G. A.; Lamb, J. D.; Christensen, J. J. Sep. Sci. Technol., in press. To be published in volume 22). Hence, the macrocycle can be retained in the membrane and can effectively extract cation(s) into the membrane.

Behr, Kirch and Lehn(9) and Fyles(Fyles, T.M.; Can. J. Chem., submitted) have shown that macrocycle-mediated cation transport in many membrane systems, including ours, is diffusion limited. The parameters affecting diffusion limited transport are the diffusion coefficient and the distribution coefficient of the transported moiety. Furthermore, the diffusion coefficients of different cation-macrocycle complexes should be similar since their structures are similar. Hence, selective cation transport is basically a function of the factors affecting the distribution coefficients of the cation complexes involved in transport.

Most of the macrocycles studied have been neutral ligands. When neutral macrocycles are used to mediate cation transport, anion(s) (A^{n-}) must accompany the cation-macrocycle complex to maintain electrical neutrality. Hence, the effect of the solvated A^{n-} on the distribution of an A^{n-}-cation-macrocycle moiety into the organic membrane from the aqueous source phase is a factor in cation transport. Previously, the largest cation transport rates were found either if A^{n-} had a small negative free energy of hydration or if the cation interacted with A^{n-} to form an ion pair(1,10). These results led us to design membrane systems for separating metal cations (M^{m+}) present in the source phase as part of A^{n-}, i.e. $AgCN_2^-$, or as a neutral M_xA_y complex.

Separation of Metals as Complex Anions. Metals present in the source phase as complex anions can often be separated in our emulsion membrane systems. Transport of such an anion requires a source phase cation to be present that either interacts with the macrocycle(11) or ion pairs with such an anion to form a moiety that is distributed to the membrane(Izatt, R. M.; Clark, G. A.; Christensen, J. J. Sep. Sci. Technol., in press. To be published in volume 22). Transport is enhanced for a particular complex anion that is less hydrated than other complex anions present. Further transport enhancement can be obtained by incorporating in the receiving phase a reagent that interacts with the metal present as part of the complex anion. These parameters lead to greater extraction of a macrocycle-cation-anion(s) complex into the membrane and maintenance of a concentration gradient in the transported species in the membrane phase, respectively(10, Izatt, R. M.; Clark, G. A.; Christensen, J. J. Sep. Sci. Technol., in press. To be published in volume 22).

Separation of Metals as Neutral Complexes. Transport of M^{m+} in this case requires that A^{n-} be present in the source phase at a concentration where a maximum amount of the cation will be present as the neutral M_xA_y species. The M_xA_y species will be weakly hydrated due to its large size and lack of charge(10). Hence, the M_xA_y species will distribute appreciably to the source phase-membrane interface where a neutral macrocycle-M_x-A_y complex can form and distribute to the membrane phase. Selective transport of a particular cation also requires that the other cations in the source phase either do not interact with A^{n-} or form highly charged anionic complexes with A^{n-} nearly quantitatively. In the case where M^{m+}-A^{n-} interaction does not occur, the co-anion must be desolvated in order for cation transport to take place. In the case where a highly charged anionic complex is formed, several cation-anion bonds must be broken for cation-macrocycle complexation to occur. In either of these cases where a thermodynamic barrier to the formation of a neutral macrocycle-cation-anion(s) moiety exists, if macrocycle-cation interaction and cation-receiving phase complexing agent interaction do not provide sufficient free energy to overcome the free energy barrier, transport of that cation will be inhibited. Therefore, a knowledge of the equilibrium constants for cation-anion interaction, cation-macrocycle interaction, and cation-receiving phase complexing agent interaction allows one to design cation selectivity into this type of membrane system.

Complete descriptions and evidence for the mechanisms involved in the A^{n-} and M_xA_y separation schemes have been reported (11, Izatt, R. M.; Bruening, R. L.; Cho, M. H.; Wu, G.; Lamb, J. D.; Christensen, J. J. J. Membr. Sci., submitted). In the present paper, examples from our recent work are presented to illustrate how A^{n-} can be used to effect interesting separations. Our earlier work and the work of others in defining and investigating other parameters involved in the transport of cations in liquid membranes have been reviewed(12,13).

Experimental

The ELM systems were formulated (Figure 1) as described previously(14). The organic phase consisted of the macrocycle DC18C6 (Figure 2) dissolved in toluene which was 3% v/v in the nonionic surfactant sorbitan monooleate (Span 80). The source phase metal cation(s) were present at 0.001 M in the NO_3^- salts for the Cd(II) vs. Zn(II) and Hg(II) transport experiments, as 0.0005 M TlAg(CN)$_2$ and 0.0005 M TlAu(CN)$_2$, or as 0.0005 M in the Br^- salts for the Ag(I) vs. Pd(II) and Au(III) transport experiments. The source phase also contained either 0.2 M Mg(SCN)$_2$, 0.0185 M MgI$_2$, 0.15 M MgBr$_2$, or 0.28 M MgCl$_2$ for the Cd(II) vs. Zn(II) and Hg(II) transport experiments, or 1.5 M KBr for the Ag(I) vs. Pd(II) and Au(III) transport experiments. The receiving phase contained either Mg(NO$_3$)$_2$, MgS$_2$O$_3$, or Li$_4$P$_2$O$_7$ for the various experiments. The sources of these compounds are available(10, Izatt, R. M.; Bruening, R. L.; Cho, M. H.; Wu, G.; Lamb, J. D.; Christensen, J. J. J. Membr. Sci., submitted, Izatt, R. M.; Clark, G. A.; Christensen, J. J. Sep. Sci. Technol., in press. To be published in volume 22, Izatt, R. M.; Bruening, R. L.; Wu, G.; Cho, M. H.; Lamb, J. D.; Christensen, J.J., in preparation). The particular Mg^{2+} or Li^+ salts were used because

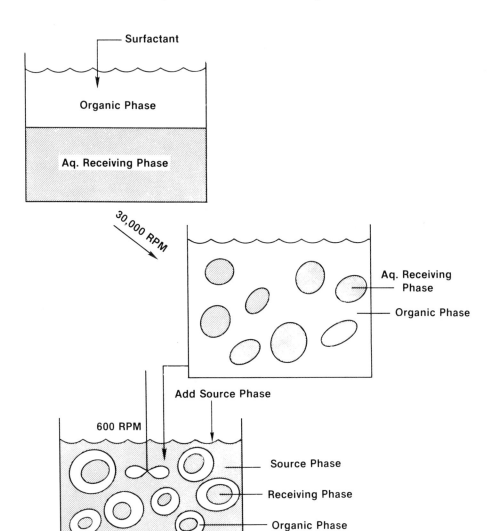

Figure 1. Formation of an emulsion liquid membrane (ELM).

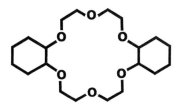

Figure 2. Structure of dicyclohexano-18-crown-6 (DC18C6).

DC18C6 forms weaker complexes with Mg^{2+} and Li^+ than with other cations. The volume ratios of the source, organic, and receiving phases were 10:1:1, respectively.

The concentrations of all metal cations present in the source phase were determined by atomic absorption spectrophotometry (Perkin-Elmer Model 603) both before and after contacting the source phase and the membrane phase for a specified time. The percent transport of the metals was then calculated from the amount of disappearance from the source phase. Each ELM experiment was done in triplicate. The standard deviations between runs average about ± 10%.

Results and Discussion

Selective Cd(II) Transport. An example of selective transport of neutral M_xA_y moieties over charged species is found in the selective transport of Cd(II) over Hg(II) and Zn(II)(Izatt, R. M.; Bruening, R. L.; Wu, G.; Cho, M. H.; Lamb, J. D.; Christensen, J.J., in preparation). In Figures 3 and 4 the fraction of Zn(II) (only Figure 3), Cd(II) and Hg(II) containing species present in aqueous solution as a neutral M_xA_y moiety, α_2, for varying concentrations of A^{n-} is given where A^{n-} = SCN^- and I^-, respectively. The curves in Figures 3 and 4 were calculated from the equilibrium constants for M^{m+}-A^{n-} interaction with the assumption made that $[A^{n-}] \gg [M^{m+}]$. In the experiments performed $[A^{n-}]$ is at least 37 times greater than $[M^{m+}]$.

When A^{n-} = SCN^-, the amount of $Cd(SCN)_2$ present in solution is maximized when $[SCN^-]$ = 0.4 M. At the same $[SCN^-]$, the amount of $Hg(SCN)_2$ present in solution is minimal, but the amount of $Zn(SCN)_2$ is nearly maximized. Therefore, as discussed in the Introduction, one would predict that Cd(II) would be transported selectively over Hg(II), but that Cd(II)-Zn(II) separation would be poor in an ELM containing 0.4 M SCN^- in the source phase. The experimental results with either NO_3^- or $S_2O_3^{2-}$ in the receiving phase are given in Table I. With NO_3^- in the receiving phase, Cd(II) is transported over Hg(II) by a factor of 75, while Cd(II) is transported over Zn(II) by a factor of only 1.8. The substitution of $S_2O_3^{2-}$ for NO_3^- in the receiving phase increases the percent transport of all 3 metals, enhances Cd(II)-Zn(II) separation, and diminishes the selectivity factor for Cd(II)-Hg(II) separation. These changes are predictable since all three metals interact with $S_2O_3^{2-}$ to a greater degree than with NO_3^- and the order of increasing interaction with $S_2O_3^{2-}$ is Zn(II), Cd(II), Hg(II). The equilibrium constants for M^{m+}-A^{n-}, M^{m+}-macrocycle, and M^{m+}-receiving phase reagent interaction are given in Table I, footnote b.

When A^{n-} = I^-, the amount of CdI_2 present in solution is maximized when $[I^-]$ = 0.037 M. At this $[I^-]$, the amount of HgI_2 present in solution is minimal. A log K value for ZnI_2 formation has not been reported and ZnI^+ formation is minimal. One would predict selective transport of Cd(II) over both Zn(II) and Hg(II) with a system containing 0.037 M I^- in the source phase. With NO_3^- in the receiving phase (Table I) Cd(II) is transported over Hg(II) by a factor of 6.4 and over Zn(II) by a factor of 26. Exchanging $S_2O_3^{2-}$ for NO_3^- in the receiving phase yields results parelleling the changes for the system where A^{n-} = SCN^-.

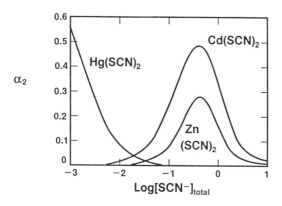

Figure 3. Fraction of M(II) present as M(SCN)$_2$, α_2, for varying [SCN$^-$]$_{total}$ where M = Zn, Cd and Hg.

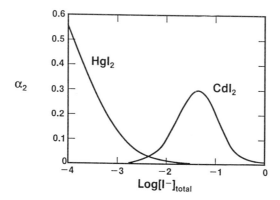

Figure 4. Fraction of M(II) present as MI$_2$, α_2, for varying [I$^-$]$_{total}$ where M = Cd and Hg.

Table I. Competitive Transport of Zn(II), Cd(II), and Hg(II)

| | | Percent Transport[a,b] | |
| | | Receiving Phase Agent | |
Metal Cation	Co-Anion	NO_3^-	$S_2O_3^{2-}$
Zn(II)	SCN^-	42	44
Cd(II)	SCN^-	75	99
Hg(II)	SCN^-	1	32
Zn(II)	I^-	3	3
Cd(II)	I^-	77	87
Hg(II)	I^-	12	98

[a]Transport after 5 minutes in a 0.4 M SCN^- or 0.037 M I^-/0.2 M DC18C6 in toluene/0.3 M $S_2O_3^{2-}$ or NO_3^- emulsion membrane. Metals are present at 0.001 M.
[b]Log $\beta_n(H_2O)$ values for formation of $M(SCN)^{2-n}$ are as follows(15). Zn(II): log β_1 = 0.71, log β_2 = 1.04, log β_3 = 1.2, log β_4 = 1.5; Cd(II): log β_1 = 1.32, log β_2 = 1.99, log β_3 = 2.0, log β_4 = 1.9; Hg(II): log β_1 = 9.08, log β_2 = 16.86, log β_3 = 19.70, log β_4 = 21.7. Log $\beta_n(H_2O)$ values for formation of MI_n^{2-n} are as follows(15). Zn(II): log β_1 = -1.5; Cd(II): log β_1 = 2.28, log β_2 = 3.92, log β_3 =5.0, log β_4 = 6.0; Hg(II): log β_1 = 12.87, log β_2 = 23.82, log β_3 = 27.6, log β_4 = 29.8. Log K values for the 1:1 interaction of M^{2+} with DC18C6 are as follows(8, Izatt, R. M.; Bruening, R. L.; Cho, M. H.; Wu, G.; Lamb, J. D.; Christensen, J. J. J. Membr. Sci., submitted, Izatt, R. M.; Bruening, R. L.; Wu, G.; Cho, M. H.; Lamb, J. D.; Christensen, J.J., in preparation). Zn(II): log K(CH_3OH) = 2.9; Cd(II): log K(CH_3OH) ~ 3.0; Hg(II): log K(H_2O) = 2.6. The Hg(II) log K value is for the cis-anti-cis isomer of DC18C6. The other data are for a mixture of isomers. Log K(CH_3OH) values are ~3 log K units above log K(H_2O) for the same reaction(16,17). All log $\beta_n(H_2O)$ values for NO_3^--M^{2+} interaction are $\leq$ 0.11 (15). Log $\beta_n(H_2O)$ values for 1:1 and 1:2 M^{2+}-$S_2O_3^{2-}$ interaction are as follows(15). Zn(II): log β_1 = 2.35; Cd(II): log β_1 =3.92, log β_2 = 6.3; Hg(II): log β_2 = 29.23.

Metal transport was not observed for any of the three metals when DC18C6 was absent from the membrane phase. Furthermore, the interaction of DC18C6 with Hg(II) is greater than that with either Cd(II) or Zn(II) (Table I). The carrier molecule appears to be essential to the transport process, although it does not determine selectivity for these particular M_xA_y moieties. Generally, one can regulate selectivity with the proper choice of macrocycle(12,13). A comparison of the four macrocycle-containing systems is instructive. Maximum Cd(II)-Hg(II) separation occurs with A^{n-} = SCN^- and without $S_2O_3^{2-}$ in the receiving phase. Maximum Cd(II)-Zn(II) separation occurs with A^{n-} = I^- and with $S_2O_3^{2-}$ in the receiving phase. However, maximum separation of Cd(II) from both Zn(II) and Hg(II) occurs with A^{n-} = I^- and without $S_2O_3^{2-}$ in the receiving phase. Furthermore, if one desires near 100% transport of Cd(II) with the best possible separation of Cd(II) from both Zn(II) and Hg(II), the system containing $S_2O_3^{2-}$ in the receiving phase and with A^{n-} = SCN^- would be the system of choice. Varying interaction of the metals with A^{n-} and $S_2O_3^{2-}$ leads to the transport differences in the systems. These data demonstrate that an ELM can be designed to perform a desired separation of metals as M_xA_y moieties if the interaction of the metals with A^{n-}, and/or a macrocycle and/or a receiving phase reagent varies significantly.

Effect of A^{n-} Solvation on M_xA_y Transport. In one ELM experiment, the $CdA_2(aq)$ (A^- = SCN^-, I^-, Br^-, or Cl^-) concentrations in the source phase were maximized ([SCN^-] = 0.4 M, [I^-] = 0.037 M, [Br^-] = 0.3 M, and [Cl^-] = 0.56 M) and Cd(II) transport(Izatt, R. M.; Bruening, R. L.; Wu, G.; Cho, M. H.; Lamb, J. D.;Christensen, J.J., in preparation) was determined after 5 minutes of source phase contact with the emulsion. The percentage of Cd(II) transported (shown in parentheses) as a function of A^- was SCN^-(82), I^- (77), Br^- (22), and Cl^- (8). The order of decreasing transport using the several A^- species is also the order of increasing degree of solvation for A^-. It appears that solvation of an M_xA_y species where M^{m+} is the same cation, but A^{n-} varies parallels solvation of free A^{n-} and is a factor in predicting M_xA_y transport rates. Hence, the choice of A^{n-} for a particular M_xA_y separation should include the consideration of this parameter.

Transport of $Au(CN)_2^-$ vs. $Ag(CN)_2^-$. The complex anions $Au(CN)_2^-$ and $Ag(CN)_2^-$ are relatively large and of similar size. Both anions have a small charge to size ratio and, hence, should be weakly hydrated(10). Transport of Tl^+ has been achieved when DC18C6 is present in the membrane phase, $Li_4P_2O_7$ is present in the receiving phase and NO_3^- is the co-anion(A^{n-}). Since $Au(CN)_2^-$ and $Ag(CN)_2^-$ should be less hydrated in aqueous solution than NO_3^- one would expect high levels of Tl^+-A^{n-} transport when A^{n-} = $Au(CN)_2^-$ or $Ag(CN)_2^-$ and this has been observed(10). Furthermore, in competitive transport experiments(10) 35% of the $Au(CN)_2^-$ transports with Tl^+ in 20 minutes when 0.01 M $Li_4P_2O_7$ is present in the receiving phase and the $Au(CN)_2^-$ is transported selectively over $Ag(CN)_2^-$ by a factor of 6. A literature search yielded no Tl^+ ion pairing data with either $Au(CN)_2^-$ or $Ag(CN)_2^-$, but we expect that significantly more ion pairing of Tl^+ with $Au(CN)_2^-$ is the explanation for the selective and rapid transport of $Au(CN)_2^-$.

Competitive Transport of $AuBr_4^-$, $AgBr_4^{3-}$ and $PdBr_4^{2-}$. Experiments comparing the competitive transport of $AuBr_4^-$ vs. $AgBr_4^{3-}$, $AuBr_4^-$ vs. $PdBr_4^{2-}$ and $AgBr_4^{3-}$ vs. $PdBr_4^{2-}$ were performed. Confirmation of the existence of $PdBr_4^{2-}$ and $AuBr_4^-$ in the original source phases was accomplished by comparing uv-visible spectra of the source phases with literature spectra. The equilibrium constants for Ag^+-Br^- interaction were used(15) to calculate that 90% of the Ag(I) in the source phase was present as $AgBr_4^{3-}$ and 10% was present as $AgBr_3^{2-}$. The other possible Ag(I) species constituted less than 1% of the total Ag(I) present. The log $\beta_n(H_2O)$ values for formation of $AgBr_n^{1-n}$(15) are log β_1 = 4.30, log β_2 = 6.64, log β_3 = 8.1 and log β_4 = 8.9. In a previous reference(Izatt, R. M.; Clark, G. A.; Christensen, J. J. Sep. Sci. Technol., in press. To be published in

Table II. Binary Competitive Transport
of $AuBr_4^-$, $PdBr_4^{2-}$, and $AgBr_4^{3-}$

Complex Anion	Membrane Phase	Percent Transport[a] Receiving Phase Agent	
		$S_2O_3^{2-}$	NO_3^-
$AgBr_4^{3-}$	0.01 M DC18C6 in toluene	47	26
$PdBr_4^{2-}$	0.01 M DC18C6 in toluene	86	15
$AgBr_4^{3-}$	toluene	6	9
$AuBr_4^-$	toluene	97	15
$PdBr_4^{2-}$	toluene	12	12
$AuBr_4^-$	toluene	99	7

[a]Transport after 15 minutes in a 1.5 M KBr/toluene/0.025 M $S_2O_3^{2-}$ or NO_3^- emulsion membrane. Metals are present at 0.0005 M.

volume 22), the Ag(I) species present was incorrectly given as $AgBr_2^-$. In the experiments involving $AuBr_4^-$, DC18C6 was not added to the membrane since a yellow precipitate formed in the source phase when DC18C6 was present. The composition of the precipitate is probably DC18C6-K^+-$AuBr_4^-$.

The data resulting from these experiments(Izatt, R. M.; Clark, G. A.; Christensen, J. J. Sep. Sci. Technol., in press. To be published in volume 22) are presented in Table II. When $S_2O_3^{2-}$ is in the receiving phase and DC18C6 is in the membrane, $PdBr_4^{2-}$ is transported selectively over $AgBr_4^{3-}$. Substitution of NO_3^- for $S_2O_3^{2-}$ results in decreased transport of both $PdBr_4^{2-}$ and $AgBr_4^{3-}$ and a reversal of their transport rates. The greater transport of $PdBr_4^{2-}$ in the $S_2O_3^{2-}$ system probably results from the much greater affinity of $S_2O_3^{2-}$ for Pd^{2+}(18) than for Ag^+(15).

In the other transport experiments, $AuBr_4^-$ was transported selectively over both $AgBr_4^{3-}$ and $PdBr_4^{2-}$ when $S_2O_3^{2-}$ was in the receiving phase. When NO_3^- was in the receiving phase, little transport was seen for any of the metals. The explanation for the high transport rates of $AuBr_4^-$ in the systems containing $S_2O_3^{2-}$ is probably two fold. First, $AuBr_4^-$ should partition more to the membrane phase as a K^+-$AuBr_4^-$ ion pair since $AuBr_4^-$ is the least hydrated of the three complex anions. This is particularly important since DC18C6 is not present to aid in the distribution of an ion pair to the membrane. Both $AuBr_4^-$ and $PdBr_4^{2-}$ are of similar size, but the smaller charge of the Au(III) species results in weaker hydration of $AuBr_4^-$. The $AgBr_4^{3-}$ species will be the most hydrated of the three species due to its large charge. Second, the large increase of $AuBr_4^-$ transport in going from the NO_3^- to the $S_2O_3^{2-}$ system suggests that Au(III)-$S_2O_3^{2-}$ interaction is similar in magnitude to Pd(II)-$S_2O_3^{2-}$ interaction. In the $PdBr_4^{2-}$-$AgBr_4^{3-}$ binary system, where $PdBr_4^{2-}$ is transported selectively, $PdBr_4^{2-}$ transport like that of $AuBr_4^-$ is greatly improved with MgS_2O_3 in the receiving phase. In these competitive systems, macrocycle-cation interaction is not transport-limiting, rather selectivity is determined by complex anion hydration and metal-receiving phase agent interaction.

Conclusion

The results presented and discussed here show that source phase co-anion type and concentration can be used to design metal separations in emulsion liquid membrane systems. Metals present in the source phase as complex anions or as neutral complexes are particularly amenable to separation design. A knowledge of the transport mechanism allows one to determine which interaction parameters are important in individual cases for the transport of metals as complex anions and neutral complexes. Source phase cation and anion free energies of hydration; cation-anion, cation-macrocycle, and cation-receiving phase agent interaction constants; and distribution coefficients between the membrane and aqueous phases for the macrocycle and macrocycle-cation-anion(s) complex are the parameters that should be known to design metal separation systems. The separations of Cd(II) from Zn(II) and Hg(II), Au(I) from Ag(I), and Au(III) from Pd(II) or Ag(I) are specific examples of the use of these principles in the design of systems for separating metals.

Acknowledgments

We gratefully acknowledge partial financial support of this study by Serpentix Corporation, Westminster, Colorado. We appreciate the help of Chris Hassell and Gypzy LindH, who made the atomic absorption analyses.

Literature Cited

1. Lamb, J. D.; Christensen, J. J.; Izatt, S. R.; Bedke, K.; Astin, M. S.; Izatt, R. M. J. Am. Chem. Soc. 1980, 102, 3399.
2. Christensen, J. J.; Christensen, S. P.; Biehl, M. P.; Lowe, S. A.; Lamb, J. D.; Izatt, R. M. Sep. Sci. Technol. 1980, 18, 363.
3. Charewicz, W. A.; Bartsch, R. A. J. Membr. Sci. 1983, 12, 323.
4. Kimura, K.; Tamura, H; Shono, T. J. Chem. Soc., Chem. Commun. 1983, 492.
5. Willis, J. P.; Young, C. C.; Olson-Mank, L.; Radle, L. Clin. Chem. 1983, 29, 1193.
6. Yamanchi, M.; Jyo, A.; Ishibashi, N. Anal. Chim. Acta 1982, 136, 299.
7. Li, N. N. U. S. patent 3 410 794, 1968. Chem.Abstr. 1969, 70, 39550.
8. Izatt, R. M.; Bradshaw, J. S.; Nelson, S. A.; Lamb, J. D.; Christensen, J. J.; Sen, D. Chem. Rev. 1985, 85, 271.
9. Behr, J.P.; Kirch, M.; Lehn, J.M. J. Am. Chem. Soc. 1985, 107, 241.
10. Izatt, R. M.; Bruening, R. L.; Clark, G. A.; Lamb, J. D.; Christensen, J. J. J. Membr. Sci. 1986, 28, 77.
11. Izatt, R. M.; Clark, G. A.; Christensen, J. J. J. Membr. Sci. 1985, 24, 1.
12. Izatt, R. M.; Clark, G. A.; Bradshaw, J. S.; Lamb, J. D.; Christensen, J. J. Sep. Purif. Methods 1986, 15, 21.

13. McBride, D. W.; Izatt, R. M.; Lamb, J. D.; Christensen, J. J. In
    Inclusion Compounds; Atwood, J. L.; Davies, J. E. D.; MacNicol,
    D. D., Eds.; Academic Press: Orlando, Florida, 1984; Vol. 3,
    Chapter 16.
14. Biehl, M. P.; Izatt, R. M.; Lamb, J. D.; Christensen, J. J. Sep.
    Sci. Technol. 1982, 17, 289.
15. Smith, R. M.; Martell, A. E. Critical Stability Constants; Plenum
    Press: New York, 1976; Vol. 4.
16. Frensdorf, H. K.; J. Am. Chem. Soc. 1971, 93, 600.
17. Izatt, R. M.; Terry, R. E.; Nelson, D. P.; Chan, Y.; Eatough, D.
    J.; Bradshaw, J. S.; Hansen, L. D.; Christensen, J. J. J. Am.
    Chem. Soc. 1976, 98, 7626.
18. Smith, R. M.; Martell, A. E. Critical Stability Constants; Plenum
    Press: New York, 1976; Vol. 5.

RECEIVED March 4, 1987

APPLICATIONS

Chapter 8

Applications of Liquid Membrane Technology

Richard D. Noble and J. Douglas Way[1]

National Bureau of Standards, Center for Chemical Engineering, Boulder, CO 80303

Commercial and laboratory applications of liquid membrane technology are discussed including gas transport, sensor development, metal ion recovery, waste
treatment, biotechnology and biomedical engineering.
Immobilized liquid membranes, emulsion or liquid surfactant membranes, and membrane reactors are discussed.
Economic data from the literature for liquid membrane
processes are presented and compared with existing
processes such as solvent extraction and cryogenic
distillation of air.

Liquid membrane and facilitated transport technology have been
studied extensively in many disciplines such as: chemical engineering, inorganic chemistry, analytical chemistry, physiology, biotechnology, and biomedical engineering. Within these disciplines, the
technology has been applied to a range of diverse applications such
as gas separations, organic removal, metals recovery, toxic waste
removal, development of selective sensing devices, enzyme reactors,
and recovery of fermentation products. Only sensors and waste removal are commerical processes although the biotechnology and metals
recovery applications seem poised for commercialization. This chapter will highlight the many applications of liquid membrane technology.

Facilitated Transport of Gases

Oxygen. Due to great biological importance, oxygen transport via a
hemoglobin carrier was one of the first facilitated transport systems studied. Scholander (1) determined the steady state oxygen
flux through an aqueous hemoglobin solutions impregnated in thin
cellulose acetate supports. He postulated a "bucket brigade" mechanism whereby the oxygen leaps from one carrier site to the next.
Wittenberg (2) studied a similar system and recognized that a mobile
carrier was necessary. He also noted that the rates of complex for-

[1]Current address: SRI International, Chemical Engineering Laboratory,
Menlo Park, CA 94025

mation and reversal were both important. Kreuzer and Hoofd (3) described the mathematical analysis assuming a facilitated transport mechanism and showed very good agreement with experimental data.
More recently, other carriers have been studied. An excellent review of this area was recently completed (4). Bend Research Inc. has recently obtained a Japanese patent for oxygen separation from air using a cobalt-salen complex. They were able to obtain O_2/N_2 selectivities in excess of 20 and an O_2 permeability of 26×10^{-9} $cm^3(STP)$-cm/cm^2-s-$cmHg$. Using a ambient pressure feed and low pressure permeate, they measured O_2 purity of 80-90 mole % (5). A major problem with synthetic carriers for oxygen at this time is that they will irreversibly oxidize at ambient conditions and, therefore, require refrigeration to maintain their reversibility. Koval and Reyes (6) discuss the chemical problems encountered with facilitated transport of oxygen.
There is considerable recent interest in preparing reactive polymer membranes with high selectivities for oxygen. Nishide et al. (7,8) covalently attached co-salen complexes to polymer membranes and observed an oxygen permeability of $17 \cdot 10^{-10} \dfrac{cm^3(STP)cm}{cm^2 \cdot s \cdot kPa}$
and an O_2/N_2 separation factor of 12. Another approach to increase the complexation site density is by polymerizing a monomer which contains a reactive Co complex (9).

Carbon Dioxide. Carbon dioxide has been studied from both a biological and an engineering perspective. One system which has received attention is the use of the bicarbonate ion as a carrier. Enns (10) established the role of the bicarbonate ion in carbon dioxide facilitated transport and demonstrated that the flux could be increased by catalyzing the reaction sequence with the enzyme carbonic anhydrase. Also, anions of weak acids such as selenite, arsenite, tellurite, and hypochlorite have been found to be effective catalysts (11,12). Ward and Robb (13) used sodium arsenite as a hydration catalyst for removing carbon dioxide from a carbon dioxide-oxygen mixture. They achieved a separation factor of 4100. The low oxygen permeability can be partially attributed to the preferential precipitation of oxidized salts in the 6 N $CsHCO_3$ membrane solution. Otto and Quinn (14) measured the carbon dioxide flux through thin bicarbonate solution films. They found the transport to be reaction rate limited in the absence of catalysts. The facilitation factor increased with increasing layer thickness and alkali metal concentration. They were able to increase the carbon dioxide flux to reaction equilibrium (diffusion-limited) values with the addition of the enzyme carbonic anhydrase. Meldon et al. (11) have shown that carbon dioxide facilitation is increased by the addition of a weak acid buffer solution. A recent review of this system has been published by Meldon et al. (15). LeBlanc et al. (16) reported facilitated carbon dioxide transport using ethylenediamine as the carrier in ion exchange membranes (IEMs). They noted the advantages of ion exchange membranes over immobilized liquid membranes. They also stated that these advantages could contribute to a longer operating life in practical gas separations under adverse high temperature and pressure conditions. Way et al. (17) also used ethylenediame as the carrier

in a perfluorsulfonic acid ion-exchange membrane. They measured
separation factors (ratio of permeabilities) of up to 551 for CO_2
over CH_4.

Carbon Monoxide. The facilitated transport of carbon monoxide by
cuprous chloride in aqueous solution was first studied by Steigelman
and Hughes (18) and more recently by Smith and Quinn (19). Smith
and Quinn found the cuprous ion to be very effective carrier for
carbon monoxide and increased the flux by two orders of magnitude
over the purely diffusive case. The facilitation factor was measured as a function of carbon monoxide partial pressure, total copper
concentration, and membrane thickness. Recently, Koval et al. (20)
reported facilitated CO transport using a ferrous complex derived
from the tetraimine macrocyclic ligand 2,3,9,10-tetramethyl-
1,3,8,11-tetraazacyclo-tetradeca-1,3,8,10- tetraene(TIM) in benzonitrile. They measured the kinetic and diffusional constants and showed selectivity for CO over a variety of other gases. The experimental and mathematical procedures which they described can be used for
any simple complexation reaction.

Hydrogen Sulfide. Matson et al. (21) utilized a carbonate solution
immobilized in a porous polymer film to study hydrogen sulfide removal for coal gasification applications. Their membrane had a high
hydrogen sulfide permeability and greater selectivity than conventional hot carbonate scrubbers. They made permeability measurements
at high temperature and pressure (363-403 K, total feed pressure 2.1
× 10^3 kPa) and observed a hydrogen sulfide permeability dependence
on carbon dioxide partial pressure. This result is reasonable since
both hydrogen sulfide and carbon dioxide can compete for the carrier.
They also studied membrane lifetime. Their apparatus was operated
continuously for periods of up to 3.6 × 10^6 s (1000 h) and no appreciable decrease in membrane permeability was observed. They also
noted that carrier deactivation due to the presence of oxygen in
coal gas was possible and that fouling due to coal tars and dust
would have to be considered in an industrial scale system.
    Kimura et al. (12) reported progress toward applying facilitat-
ed transport membranes to industrial scale separations. They measured carbon dioxide and hydrogen sulfide permeabilities at industrially significant operating conditions (6.90 × 10^2 kPa CO_2, 363-403
K). Under these conditions, the authors determined that carbon dioxide transport is influenced by both diffusion and reaction rates.
They also noted that hydrogen sulfide selectivity over carbon dioxide can be improved by introducing gas gaps in a multilayer membrane
because of the higher reaction rates of hydrogen sulfide. They
found that catalysts increased the carbon dioxide hydration rate by
a factor of 2 at low carbon dioxide partial pressure, this effect
was observed to increase as carbon dioxide partial pressure decreased. Economic studies based on experimental data indicate that
cost savings on the order of 30-50% over conventional acid gas scrub-
bing were possible with immobilized liquid membranes.
    Way and Noble (22) reported facilitated transport of H_2S in ion
exchange membranes containing organic diamine cations at ambient
conditions. The IEMs were highly selective for H_2S over CH_4 and had

high H_2S permeabilities. Separation factors for H_2S/CH_4 up to 1200 were measured corresponding to an H_2S permeability of $4632 \cdot 10^{-10}$

$$\frac{cm^3(STP)cm}{cm^2 \cdot s \cdot kPa}.$$

Olefins. Facilitated transport of olefins has also been reported in the literature. LeBlanc et al. ([16]) studied ethylene transport using a silver ion carrier in an ion exchange membrane. Hughes et al. ([23]) presented the results of a bench and pilot scale study of ethylene and propylene transport using a silver ion immobilized in anisotropic, porous hollow fiber membranes. This work is very significant because it is the first report facilitated transport membranes used on a commercial scale. Teremoto et al. ([24]) also studied ethylene transport with a silver ion carrier in a supported liquid membrane. They found a selectivity for ethylene over ethane of approximately 1000 when the silver nitrate concentration was 4 mol/dm^2.

Nitric Oxide. Nitric oxide facilitated transport using a ferrous ion as carrier has been reported. Ward ([25]) carried out an experimental and mathematical investigation of this system. He measured the NO flux through a liquid layer immobilized between two thin polymeric films. His mathematical analysis showed that the system was not operating in either diffusion-limited or reaction-limited regions but somewhere in between. In a further investigation, Ward ([26]) observed that NO could be transported across a ferrous chloride film against a NO concentration gradient by applying a voltage difference across the film. Bdzil et al. ([27]) presented a mathematical analysis of electrically induced carrier transport for this system.

Sensors. Bard and Faulkner ([28]) review applications of immobilized liquid and facilitated transport membranes to the design of electrodes for the detection of cations and anions in aqueous solutions. Deetz ([29]) describes the fabrication of liquid membrane based sensors for organic vapors.

Liquid Phase Systems

Immobilized Liquid Membranes (ILM). Metal ion separation for hydrometallurgical applications has received considerable interest ([30]). Babcock, Baker, and coworkers ([31]-[34]) have studied coupled transport of metal ions using supported liquid membranes. Porous polypropylene flat sheet membranes and porous polymer hollow fiber membranes were impregnated with a hydrocarbon solvent containing an appropriate carrier. The applications considered were the control of heavy metal pollutants, and the recovery of copper, uranium, and cobalt. Baker et al. ([32]) discussed work on supported liquid membranes for copper transport. Copper was transported against a 4000 fold concentration difference using a beta-hydroxyoxime carrier from a mixture of copper and iron ions and a separation factor of 1000 for copper over iron was observed. Typical transport rates were approximately 5.0×10^{-7} kg Cu/(m^2-s). Uranium transport using a tertiary amine complexing agent under similar conditions was

reported by Babcock et al. (33,34). The principal factors affecting
the uranium flux were the uranium ion concentration and the pH of
the aqueous phase, concentration of the carrier, pore size
distribution of the supporting membrane and the solubility of the
uranium carrier complex in the organic solvent. The maximum flux
was obtained at 30 volume % carrier. They postulated that the
solubility of the complex limited the reaction rate. The authors
observed two types of interfacial effects; concentration
polarization at the aqueous phase-membrane interface and transport
rate limitation by the rate of complexation at the interface.
Danesi et al. (35) studied cadmium and zinc transport using a
carrier. A historical development of coupled transport is given by
Babcock et al. (36).

Danesi and Cianetti (37,38) and Danesi and Reichley-Yinger
(1986) described the use of multiple membranes to perform metal extraction. The separation can be increased by staging the membranes.
The use of composite membranes is also discussed whereby each seg-
ment of the composite can perform a specific function.

Chiarizia et al. (39) described the influence of carrier dimeri-
zation on metal extraction. They noted this effect on overall membrane permeability but this effect can be incorporated in any measure of membrane transport.

The use of ILMs for the separation of fermentation products
such as acetic and citric acid has been recently reported by several
investigators. Kuo and Gregor (40) and Kiani et al. (41) used immobilized liquid membranes to extract acetic acid from aqueous solutions. While Kuo and Gregor (40) did demonstrate the concept of
facilitated transport of acetic acid, the permeation rates they reported were quite low. Babcock et al. (42) reported the extraction
of citric acid from actual fermentation broth. The effects of
temperature, agent-solution composition, and citric acid
concentration on transport rates were investigated.

In another biotechnology application, Matson (43) coined the
term "membrane reactor" to refer to the integration of the reaction,
separation, and concentration steps of an enzymatic conversion reaction. A sandwich of a permselective ILM and a catalytic membrane
was used to allow the diffusion of the reactant into the catalytic
membrane and to limit the diffusion of the product of the enzymatic
reaction of the membrane. A high feed stream flowrate to product
stream flowrate ratio was used to concentrate the product.

Danesi (44) reported on an ILM using a carrier molecule as an
electron carrier. This allows one to use redox reactions to transport charge as well as mass.

Danesi et al. (45) studied the lifetime of the ILMs for liquid
phase extractions. Correlations were established among the following factors: the lifetime of the ILM's, their interfacial and water
extraction properties, the concentrations of the feed and strip solutions adjacent to the ILM and the ability of the ILM to transport
water.

The following conclusions were reached about the stability of
ILM's: (i) when the electrolyte concentrations of the aqueous solutions separated by the membrane are approximately equal and the solubility of the organic carrier in water is low, stable ILM's are obtained, (ii) when the electrolyte concentrations of these aqueous

solutions are very different, resulting in a large osmotic pressure gradient, ILM's become unstable and their lifetime decreases with the applied osmotic pressure gradient, the amount of water extracted and the wettability of the ILM, (iii) the ability of ILM's to transport water parallels their instability and the amount of water transported can be taken as an indication of instability.

Emulsion Liquid Membranes (ELM). Metal ion extraction using emulsion liquid membranes has received considerable interest (46). Martin and Davies (47) evaluated the feasibility of using emulsion liquid membranes to recover copper ions from dilute aqueous solutions. They studied factors influencing mass transfer such as membrane composition, pH and acid content of the feed and internal phase, and agitation rate. At low breakage levels, their mass transfer data could be represented by a pseudo first order process. Kondo et al. (48) formulated emulsion liquid membranes for recovering copper ions. A water-in-oil emulsion was prepared with HCl in the inner aqueous phase and copper chelating agent such as benzoylacetone in the organic phase. They studied the rates of complex formation and effect of process variables such as agitation speed, continuous phase pH, carrier concentration, surfactant concentration, and treat ratio (ratio of the emulsion volume to the continuous phase volume) on the mass transfer rate. Their experimental results showed that the initial extraction rate of copper was inversely proportional to the square root of the hydrogen ion concentration in the continuous phase and directly proportional to the carrier concentration. The authors found that the extraction rate of copper could be explained by a pseudo first order dependency with respect to the copper concentration. It was postulated that the overall extraction rates were controlled by the complex formation reaction rate and diffusion in the concentration boundary layer. Cahn et al. (49) also studied copper extraction using emulsion liquid membranes. They studied the effect of membrane parameters and properties such as bulk viscosity, carrier concentration, treat ratio and internal droplet leakage. The bulk viscosity of hydrocarbon membrane phase was measured. They found that the mass transfer rate was retarded and leakage was reduced by increased viscosity. Data from pilot plant tests were used to calculate process economics for a plant to recover copper with emulsion liquid membranes. Compared to solvent extraction, they concluded that the liquid membrane process could be up to 40% less expensive. The major cost reduction was in capital expenditures. Volkel et al. (50) studied copper extraction and found that they could concentrate copper 500:1 using ELMs. Weiss and Grigoriev (51) and Boyadhiev and Benzenshek (52) studied mercury removal from wastewater. Hochhauser and Cussler (53) concentrated chromium with ELMs. Fuller and Li (54) reported on chromium and zinc extraction from cooling water blowdown. Uranium extraction has also been reported (55).

Substantial work has been done to investigate the use of macrocyclic polyethers to facilitate the transport of metal ions by Christensen, Izatt and Lamb (56-59). These carriers were incorporated into both bulk liquid and emulsion liquid membranes for the transport of mono- and divalent cations. They have developed a

model which describes the effect on metal ion transport of various
parameters including the metal binding constant with the carriers.
Recently, Bartsch and coworkers (60-64) have developed ionizable
macrocycles. This development allows for ion transport without having to consider the counterion. Their studies indicate that the
ionizable crown ethers have increased flux and selectivity. An extensive review of this topic has recently been published (65).
Cussler and coworkers reported some of the earliest results in this
area (53,66,67). Caracciolo et al. (68) showed that a macrocyclic
polyether can pump a cation against its concentration gradient.
They explained this phenomenon in terms of ion pair transport. Lee
et al. (69) studied copper extraction using two types of liquid membranes. More recently, Gokalp et al. (70) used liquid membranes
containing polyethers to electrorefine silver and copper. They ex-
plored two geometries for the liquid membrane. They placed the membrane between the anode and cathode and also coated the cathode with
the membrane in separate experiments. They were able to demonstrate
the technical feasibility of this process.

A recent study with biotechnology applications relates to amino
acid extraction. Schugerl and co-workers (71) used a quaternary
ammonium carrier in an emulsion liquid membrane system for enzyme
catalyzed preparation of L-amino acids. Frankenfield et al. (72)
discuss a wide variety of biomedical ELM applications including enzyme encapsulation, blood oxygenation, and treatment of chronic
uremia.

Emulsion liquid membranes have been formulated for the removal
of species without chemical carriers. These systems rely on solubility differences between permeant species. The first work performed
by Li (73) dealt with the separation of a binary mixture of aromatic
and paraffinic hydrocarbons. The hydrocarbons were encapsulated in
an aqueous liquid membrane forming an emulsion which was distributed
in a hydrocarbon solvent and mixed. The aromatic hydrocarbons
preferentially permeated through the aqueous liquid membrane phase
due to solubility differences. Cahn and Li (74) describe a liquid
membrane formulation for phenol removal in which sodium hydroxide is
encapsulated by an organic liquid membrane. The resulting membrane
phase is mixed with a continuous aqueous phase containing phenol.
The aromatic hydrocarbon can diffuse through the liquid membrane
into the inner aqueous phase. The phenol is then neutralized to
sodium phenolate which, being insoluble in the organic membrane, is
trapped in the inner phase. Thus, a high phenol concentration gradient was constantly maintained across the liquid membrane. Halwachs
et al. (75) reported on the removal of phenol and other organic solutes. Terry et al. (76) presented further work on removing phenol
and organic acids including mixtures using ELM technology. Teremoto
et al. (77) studied phenol and cresol extraction with ELMs.
Boyadzhiev et al. (78) discussed phenol extraction using a combined
ELM and film pertraction scheme. Volkel et al. (79) discuss an interesting application. They used an enzyme encapsulated in an ELM
to remove phenol from blood. Kitagawa et al. (80) discussed applications of the liquid membrane technique to the removal of ammonia
and various metal ions from industrial waste water. For ammonia
removal, the formulation used was similar to that for phenol separation except that the trapping agent was an acid. Various commercial

ion exchange reagents were employed as carriers for the metal separations. Baird et al. (81) recently reported various amine extractions using HCl in the internal phase to trap the amine. They reported both single component and binary data.

Cui et al. (82) recently reported on a new approach in ELM technology. They use one species as both carrier and surfactant. Normally, separate species are used.

Industrial Applications of Liquid Membrane Technology

Emulsion Liquid Membranes. Bock et al. (83) and Hayworth et al. (84) reported on the application of emulsion liquid membrane technology to the recovery of uranium from wet process phosphoric acid. The hydrocarbon phase of the ELM consisted of a mixture of di-2-ethylhexyl phosphoric acid (DEHPA) and trioctyl phosphine oxide (TOPO) as carriers, and a pipsapolyamine surfactant in a paraffinic-aromatic hydrocarbon solvent. The aqueous internal phase of the emulsion contained a strippling solution of phosphoric acid with a reducing agent capable of producing U^{4+} from U^{6+}. The authors concluded that the economics of the liquid membrane process were superior to solvent extraction. The economic study was based on data from a 0.06 m^3/h continuous pilot plant operated in South Pierce, Florida. Single and two stage countercurrent experimental runs were used to confirm a three countercurrent extractor design capable of greater than 90% recovery with a 6 g/L internal phase uranium concentration. The capital costs of the ELM design were equivalent to solvent extraction with minimum feed pretreatment and superior to solvent extraction when extensive feed pretreatment was required. The operating cost estimate for the ELM plant was $40.2/kg compared to $55.2-56.0/kg U_3O_8 for solvent extraction.

Frankenfeld et al. (85) reported a similar study on the recovery of copper with ELM technology. The ELM used had a typical hydrocarbon phase formulation of 2.0 mass % nonionic polyamine surfactant, 2.5% beta hydroxyoxime carrier, and the balance isoparaffinic hydrocarbon solvent. The internal aqueous phase of the emulsion was approximately 20 mass % H_2SO_4. Using a basis of a 2.7×10^7 kg Cu/year plant, it was estimated that the liquid membrane plant would save 40% in capital costs with nearly identical operating costs.

Marr (86) discussed the application of ELM technology to remove zinc as zinc sulfate from low concentration wastewater from a textile plant in Lenzing, Austria. In the six month pilot plant study, 1000 m^3/h of wastewater was treated more economically with liquid membranes than solvent extraction due to the low Zn concentration. The plant used proprietary countercurrent extraction columns and electrostatic coalescers to break the emulsion prior to Zn recovery and organic phase recycle.

A commercial plant for Zn removal at the same location has been in operation since the end of 1986 and is meeting all design goals, including Zn removal and throughput. The Zn concentration in the aqueous stream is reduced from less than 1 g/l to ppm levels in less than 20 minutes average residence time in the extraction column (87). Concentrations in the inner droplet phase of the ELM of up to 50 g/l Zn are obtained. Proprietary design countercurrent extraction columns (10 m high, 1.5 m diameter) are used. The plant throughput is 75 to 100 m³/hr. Emulsion stability is the major processing consideration.

Immobilized Liquid Membranes. A pilot plant study of the recovery of ethylene and propylene from a polypropylene reactor off-gas stream was presented by Hughes et al. (23). Aqueous solutions of Ag^+ ion were immobilized in the pore structure of commercial reverse osmosis hollow fiber modules. The pilot plant operated at feed pressures of 414-827 kPa, feed flow rates of 1.42-4.25 m³/h at STP, and sweep flow rates of 3.79×10^{-2} - 0.114 m³/h hexane. Permeate streams with propylene concentrations in excess of 98 mole % were observed in pilot plant operation with modules containing 22.3 to 37.2 m² membrane area.

Babcock (88) discussed efforts to commercialize an ILM process to produce oxygen-enriched air. The spiral-wound modules contain an ILM consisting of a cobalt based carrier molecule in a low volatility organic solvent immobilized in a 4 μm thick microporous film. The oxygen carrier has a 3 to 4 week lifetime at ambient temperature. Longer lifetimes were obtained at subambient temperatures. Optimized ILM modules produced 80 to 90 % O_2 in a single pass. In long term tests, the product gas purity exceeded 70% for as long as three months. Atmospheric CO_2 was observed to reduce the membrane lifetime. The membrane has a separation factor of 25 (O_2 permeability/ N_2 permeability) and achieves a flux of 5.34×10^{-8} gmol/(cm²-s). A product stream of 80% O_2 can be produced from air at a cost of $93.6/1000 kg ($85/ton) O_2. An economic study indicated that a flux of $2.4 \cdot 10^{-7}$ gmol/(cm²·s) is needed if the ILM process can compete favorably with ton quantities of O_2 produced by cryogenic distillation.

Babcock (89) also reported pilot plant uranium and chromium recovery projects using ILMs. Membrane modules were constructed with hollow fiber polysulfone supports containing kerosene solutions of commercially available hydrometallurgical complexation agents such as tertiary amines. Operating costs for the extraction step calculated from uranium recovery data were $0.8/kg Ur for a 3.8×10^3 m³/day plant which were superior to costs associated with solvent extraction and ion-exchange.

Conclusions

Currently, the only commercial process application of liquid membrane technology is waste treatment, where low concentration solutes must be removed from large volumes of effluents. Conventional technology such as solvent extraction and ion exchange is often marginally economic at these conditions. Due to the presence of the complexation reaction and the low volume of liquid membrane required for either emulsion or immobilized configurations, liquid membrane technology is ideally suited for high recoveries of dilute solutes as demonstrated by the commercialization of ELM technology for Zn removal in Austria.

Liquid membranes are being used commercially in the production of ion selective electrodes for many aqueous cations and anions. Recently, Deetz (29) described the use of liquid membrane technology for the fabrication of gas sensors selective for organic vapors.

These membranes have a selectivity of over $10^5:1$ for acetone over water vapor.

Despite very promising technical performance, few processes have been commercialized. This fact probably stems from a number of economic factors, especially the depressed state of the non ferrous metals industry. Several liquid membrane pilot studies for U, Cr, and Cu had more favorable economics than solvent extraction, but very few new plants will be built in poor economic climates. This obviates the present need for new technology, regardless of its technical or economic superiority.

The long term stability of liquid membranes of either the emulsion or immobilized configuration promises to be an important issue that may limit the commercialization of liquid membrane technology. Babcock's (89) ILM pilot plant for uranium recovery operated successfully for 200-250 days before requiring a recharge of solvent and complexing agent. Such long term studies are necessary to establish industrial confidence in the technology.

Research is necessary to develop new complexation chemistry to increase the number of separations possible with liquid membrane technology and to improve existing processes. Related theoretical work could define the set of properties required to optimize the separation and provide guidelines for improving existing complexation reactions. Improved thin film technology would definitely speed industrial application of liquid membrane technology, especially in gas separation applications. Improved supports and immobilization techniques are necessary in order to fabricate ILMs and ion exchange membranes in thicknesses of a few μm or less to produce economically attractive fluxes.

Literature Cited

1. Scholander, P.F. Science 1960, 131, 585.
2. Wittenberg, J.B. J. Biol. Chem. 1966, 241, 104.
3. Kreuzer, F. and Hoofd, L. Resp. Phys. 1970, 8, 280-302.
4. Niederhoffer, E.C., Timmons, J.H., and Martell, A.E. Chem. Rev. 1984, 84(2), 137-203.
5. Johnson, B.M., Baker, R.W., Matson, S.L., Smith, K.L., Roman, I.C., Tuttle, M.E., and Lonsdale, H.K., J. Mem. Sci., in press.
6. Koval, C.A. and Reyes, Z., ibidem.
7. Nishide, H., Ohyanagi, M., Okada O., and Tsuchelda, E., Macromolecules 1986, 19, 496-498.
8. Nishide, H., Kuwahara, M., Ohyanagi, M., Funada, Y., Kawakami, H. and Tsuchida, E. Chem. Letters, Chem. Soc. of Japan 1986, 43-46.
9. Sterzel H.J., Sanner, A., Neumann, P., U.S. Patent No. 4,584, 359, 1986.
10. Enns, T. Science 1967, 155, 44-47.
11. Meldon, J.H., Smith, D.A., and Colton, C.K. Chem. Eng. Sci. 1977, 32, 939.
12. Kimura, S.G., Matson, S.L., and Ward, W.J. III. In Recent Developments in Separation Science; N.N. Li, Ed.; CRC Press, 1979; Vol. 5.
13. Ward, W.J. III and Robb, W.L. Science 1967, 156, 1481-1484.
14. Otto, N.C. and Quinn, J.A. Chem. Eng. Sci. 1971, 26, 949-961.

15. Meldon, J.H., Stroeve, P., and Gregoire, C.K. Chem. Eng. Comm. 1982, 16, 263.
16. LeBlanc, O.H., Ward, W.J., Matson, S.L., and Kimura, S.G., J. Mem. Sci. 1980, 6, 339.
17. Way, J.D., Noble, R.D., Reed, D.L., and Ginley, G.M., A.I.Ch.E.J. 1987, in press.
18. Steigelman, E.F. and Hughes, R.D. (1973). U.S. Patent 3,758,603.
19. Smith, D.R. and Quinn, J.A. A.I.Ch.E. J. 1980, 26, 112.
20. Koval, C.A, Noble, R.D., Way, J.D., Louie, B., Reyes, A., Horn, G. and Reed, D. Inorgan. Chem. 1985, 24, 1147-1152.
21. Matson, S.L., Herrick, C.S., and Ward, W.J. III I&EC Proc. Des. Dev. 1977, 16, 370.
22. Way, J.D. and Noble, R.D. ibidem.
23. Hughes, R.D., Mahoney, J.A. and Steigelmann, E.F., Recent Developments in Separation Science, CRC Press, 1986; Vol. IX, pp 173-195.
24. Teremoto, M., Matsuyama, H., Yamashiro, T. and Katayama, Y. J. Chem. Eng. Japan 1986, 19, 419-424.
25. Ward, W.J. III. A.I.Ch.E. J. 1970a, 16, 405-410.
26. Ward, W.J. III. Nature 1970b, 227, 162-163.
27. Bdzil, J., Carlier, C.C., Irisch, H.L., Ward, W.J., and Breiter, M.W., J. Phys. Chem. 1973, 77, 846.
28. Bard A.J. and Faulkner, L.R., Electrochemical Methods 1980, J. Wiley & Sons, Inc.
29. Deetz, D., Proceedings of 4th International Conf. on Indoor Air Quality and Climate, Berlin, FRG, Aug. 17-21, 1987.
30. Kim, K. J. Mem. Sci. 1984, 21, 5-10.
31. Babcock, W.C., Baker, R.W., Kelly, D.J., Kleiber, J.C., and Lonsdale, H.K. (1979b). Coupled Transport Systems for Control of Heavy Metal Pollutants. EPA Report No. R804682-01.
32. Baker, R.W., Tuttle, M.E., Kelly, D.J., and Lonsdale, H.K. J. Mem. Sci. 1977, 2, 213.
33. Babcock, W.C., Baker, R.W., LaChapelle, E.D., and Smith, K.L. J. Mem. Sci. 1980a, 7, 71-87.
34. Babcock, W.C., Baker, R.W., LaChapelle, E.D., and Smith, K.L. J. Mem. Sci. 1980b, 7, 89-100.
35. Danesi, P.R., Chiarizia, R., and Castagnola, A. J. Mem. Sci. 1983, 14: 161-174.
36. Babcock, W.C., Kelly, D.J., LaChapelle, E.D., Smith, K.L., and Baker, R.W. Proceedings of Hydrometallurgy; Society of Chemical Industry, Manchester, England, 1981.
37. Danesi, P.R. and Cianetti, C. J. Mem. Sci. 1984a, 20, 201-214.
38. Danesi, P.R. and Cianetti, C. J. Mem. Sci. 1984b, 20, 215-226.
39. Charewicz, W.A. and Bartsch, R.A., J. Mem. Sci. 1983, 12, 323-333.
40. Kuo, Y. and Gregor, H.P., Sep. Sci. Tech. 1983, 18(15), 421-440.
41. Kiani, A, Bhave, R.R., and Sirkar, K.K., J. Mem. Sci. 1984, 20, 125-145.
42. Babcock, W.C., Brose, D.J., Chambers, A.R., and Friesen, D.T., J. Mem. Sci. 1987, in press.
43. Matson, S.L. (1979) University of Pennsylvania. Ph.D. Thesis.
44. Danesi, P.R., J. Mem. Sci. 1986, 29, 2.

45. Danesi, P.R., Reichley-Yener, L., Rickert, P.G., J. Mem. Sci. 1987, in press.
46. Izatt, R.M., Dearden, D.V., McBride, Jr., D.M., Oscarson, J.L., Lamb, J.D., and Christensen, J.J., Sep. Sci. Tech. 1983, 18, 1113-1129.
47. Martin, T.P. and Dvaies, G.A., Hydrometallurgy 1977, 2, 315.
48. Kondo, K., Kita, K., Koida, I., Irie, J., and Nakashio, F., J. Chem. Eng. Japan 1979, 12, 203.
49. Cahn, R.P., Frankenfeld, J.W., and Li, N.N. Extraction of Copper with Liquid Membranes; Paper presented at A.I.Ch.E. Mtg., Chicago, IL., Nov. 1980.
50. Volkel, W., Halwachs, W., and Schugerl, K. J. Mem. Sci. 1980, 6, 19-31.
51. Weiss, S. and Grigoriev V. J. Mem. Sci. 1982, 12, 119-129.
52. Boyadzhiev, L., and Bezenshek E. J. Mem. Sci. 1983, 14, 13-18.
53. Hochhauser, A.M. and Cussler, E.L. A.I.Ch.E. Symp. Ser. 1975, 71(152), 136-142.
54. Fuller, E.J. and Li, N.N. J. Mem. Sci. 1984, 18, 251-272.
55. Boch, J. and Valint, P.L. I&EC Fund 1982, 21, 417.
56. Christensen, J.J., Izatt, R.M., and Lamb, J.D. Selective transport of Metal Ions Through Liquid Membranes Containing Macrocyclic Carriers; Papers presented at A.I.Ch.E. Mtg., Chicago, IL., Nov. 1980.
57. Izatt, R.M., Lamb, J.D., Swain, C.S., Christensen, J.J., and Haymore, B.L. J. Amer. Chem. Soc. 1980, 102, 3032.
58. Lamb, J.D., Christensen, J.J., Izatt, S.R. Bedke, K., Astin, M.S., and Izatt, R.M. J. Amer. Chem. Soc. 1980a, 102, 3399.
59. Lamb, J.D., Christensen, J.J., Osearson, J.L., Nielsen, B.L., Asay, B.W., and Izatt, R.M. J. Amer. Chem. Soc. 1980b, 6820.
60. Strzelbicki, J. and Bartsch, R.A. J. Mem. Sci. 1982, 10, 35-47.
61. Charewicz, W.A., Heo, G.S., and Bartsch, R.A. Anal. Chem. 1982, 54, 2094-2097.
62. Charewicz, W.A. and Bartsch, R.A. Anal. Chem. 1982, 54, 2300-2302.
63. Charewicz, W.A. and Bartsch, R.A. J. Mem. Sci. 1983, 12, 323-333.
64. Barsch, R.A., Charewicz, W.A., and Kang S.I. J. Mem. Sci. 1984, 17, 97-107.
65. Izatt, R.M., Clark, G.A., Bradshaw, J.S., Lamb, J.D., and Christensen, J.J. Sep. Pur. Meth. 1986, 15(1), 21-72.
66. Cussler, E.L. Evans, D.F., and Matesich, M.A. Science 1971, 172, 377-379.
67. Reusch, C.F. and Cussler, E.L. A.I.Ch.E. J. 1973, 19, 736-741.
68. Caracciolo, F., Cussler, E.L., and Evans, D.F., A.I.Ch.E. J. 1975, 21, 160-167.
69. Lee, K.H., Evans, D.F., and Cussier, E.L. A.I.Ch.E. J. 1978, 24, 860.
70. Gokalp, M., Hodgson, K.T., and Cussler, E.L. J. Phys. Chem. 1985, 89, 1825-1830.
71. Makryaleas, K., Scheper, T., Schugerl, K., and Kula, M.R. Chem. Ing. Tech. 1985, 57, 362-363.

72. Frankenfeld, J.W., Asher, W.J., and Li, N.N. Recent Developments in Separation Science; N.N. Li, Ed.; Chemical Rubber Co; 1978; Vol. 4, p 39.

73. Li, N.N. I&EC Proc. Des. Dev. 1971, 10, 215-221.

74. Cahn, R.P. and Li, N.N. Membrane Separation Processes; P. Meares, Ed., Elsevier Pub. Co., 1976.

75. Halwachs, W., Flaschel, E. and Schugerl, K. J. Mem. Sci. 1980, 6, 33-44.

76. Terry, R.E., Li, N.N., and Ho, W.S. J. Mem. Sci. 1982, 10, 305-323.

77. Teremoto, M., Takihana, H., Shibutani, M., Yussa, T., and Hara, N. Sep. Sci. Tech. 1983a, 18, 397-420.

78. Boyadzhiev, L. Bezenshek E. J. Mem. Sci. 1983, 14, 13-18.

79. Volkel, W., Poppe, W., halwachs, W., and Schugerl, K. J. Mem. Sci. 1982, 11, 333-347.

80. Kitigawa, T., Nishikawa, J., Frankenfeld, J., and Li, N.N. Envir. Sci. Tech. 1977, 11, 602.

81. Baird, R.S., Bunge, A.L., and Noble, R.D., A.I.Ch.E. J. 1987, 33(1), 43-53.

82. Cui, F., Tang, B., Xu, M., Qi, Q., and Zhu, L. J. Mem. Sci. 1985, 23, 137-154.

83. Bock, J., Klein, R.R., Valint, P.L., and Ho, W.S. Liquid Membrane Extraction of Uranium from Wet Process Phosphoric Acid-Field Process Demonstration; Paper presented at A.I.Ch.E. Met., New Orleans, La. Nov. 1981.

84. Hayworth, H.C., Ho, W.S., Burns, W.A., and Li, N.N. Sep. Sci. Tech. 1983, 18, 493-520.

85. Frankenfeld, J.W., Cahn, R.P., and Li, N.N. Sep. Sci. Tech. 1981, 16, 385-402.

86. Marr, R. Pilot Plant Studies of Liquid Membrane Separations; Paper presented at the Engineering Foundation Conference on New Directions in Separation Technology, Davos, Switzerland, Oct. 1984.

87. Draxler, J., Fiirst, W., and Marr, R., Proceedings of the International Solvent Extraction Conference; 1986; Vol. 1, pp 553-560.

88. Babcock, W.C. Liquid Membranes for the Production of Oxygen-Enriched Air; Paper presented at the U.S. Dept. of Energy Membrane Technology Res. & Dev. Workshop, Clemson Univ., Clemson, S.C., Oct. 1984.

89. Babcock, W.C., LaChapelle, E.D., and Kelly, D.J. Coupled Transport Membranes for Heavy Metal Recovery; Paper presented at the A.I.Ch.E. Mtg., Denver, Co. Aug. 1983, paper no. 60e.

RECEIVED May 11, 1987

Chapter 9

Hydrogen Sulfide Facilitated Transport in Perfluorosulfonic Acid Membranes

J. Douglas Way[1] and Richard D. Noble

National Bureau of Standards, Center for Chemical Engineering, Boulder, CO 80303

Hydrogen sulfide and methane fluxes were measured at ambient conditions for 200 μm perfluorosulfonic acid cation exchange membranes containing monopositive EDA counterions as carriers. Facilitation factors up to 26.4 and separation factors for H_2S/CH_4 up to 1200 were observed. The H_2S transport is diffusion limited. The data are well represented by a simplified reaction equilibrium model. Model predictions indicate that H_2S facilitated transport would be diffusion limited even at a membrane thickness of 1 μm.

Reversible complexation reactions have long been used to improve the speed and selectivity of separation processes, especially those involving the separation or purification of dilute solutes (1). Such reactions are the basis of a multitude of separation unit operations including gas absorption, solvent extraction, and extractive distillation. When a reversible complexation reaction (carrier) is incorporated into a membrane, the performance of the membrane can be improved through a process known as facilitated transport. In this process, shown schematically in Figure 1, there are two pathways available for the transport of the solute through the membrane. The solute can permeate through the membrane by a solution-diffusion mechanism and by the diffusion of the solute-carrier complex. Other solutes are not bound by the carrier due to the specificity of the complexation reaction; this increases the selectivity of the process.

Facilitated transport of gases has been the subject of numerous investigations which are summarized in recent review articles (2-3). Immobilized liquid membranes (ILMs) were prepared for the majority of these studies by impregnating the pore structure of very thin, microporous polymeric substrates with a solution of a solvent and a complexation agent (4). Such ILMs have two primary experimental problems: loss of solvent phase and loss or deactivation of the com-

---

[1]Current address: SRI International, Chemical Engineering Laboratory, Menlo Park, CA 94025

plexation agent or carrier. Solvent loss occurs when solvent evaporates or is forced from the support pore structure by large trans-membrane pressures. Carrier loss can occur when solvent in the feed stream condenses on the feed side of the membrane and is forced through the pore structure due to a pressure gradient which would leach out the carrier. Irreversible reaction of the carrier with impurities in the feed or product gas stream could lead to deactivation or breakdown of the carrier.

A recent approach has been to use ion exchange membranes (IEMs) as a support for complexation agents (5-6). A cationic or anionic carrier is exchanged into an appropriate nonporous IEM to form the facilitated transport membrane. This configuration has the advantage that the carrier cannot easily be forced out of the support since the carrier is retained by strong electrostatic forces. IEM supports may provide longer operating lifetimes where conventional ILMs may be subject to carrier or solvent loss.

In this study, monopositive ethylene diamine (EDA) ions were exchanged into perfluorosulfonic acid (PFSA) ionomer films to prepare facilitated transport membranes. The flux of H_2S was measured with and without carrier present at ambient conditions as a function of H_2S mole fraction in the feed gas stream. The selectivity of these membranes was determined by simultaneous measurements of H_2S and CH_4 fluxes from binary mixtures as a function of composition. Reaction equilibrium models were derived to predict the observed experimental data.

Background

Facilitated transport of H_2S was first demonstrated by Ward (7) in immobilized HCO_3^-/CO_3^{2-} solutions at ambient conditions. Matson et al. (8) reported progress in the development of facilitated transport membranes to remove H_2S from gasified coal. Their membrane used a carbonate solution immobilized in a porous polymer film. A comparison between the membrane transport data and conventional hot potassium carbonate absorption processes indicated that the ILM had greater H_2S/CH_4 selectivity than the absorption process. The authors measured H_2S permeability at high temperature and pressure (363-403 K, total feed pressure 2.1×10^3 kPa) and observed a dependence of H_2S permeability on CO_2 partial pressure in the feed gas stream. This observation is reasonable since CO_2 transport is facilitated by HCO_3^-/CO_3^{2-} liquid membranes, and CO_2 would be competing with H_2S for carrier molecules. Studies were also made of membrane longevity. Their apparatus was operated continuously for periods of up to 1000 h, and no appreciable decrease in membrane permeability was observed. It was noted that acute carrier deactivation due to the presence of oxygen in the coal gas was possible and that fouling due to coal tars and dust would have to be considered in an industrial scale system.

H_2S-EDA Chemistry. The basis of facilitated transport is the selective, reversible reaction of a carrier molecule with the solute to be separated. Consequently, it is important to select a carrier with appropriate properties to produce the desired selectivity toward one or more components in a mixture. Many complexation reactions for H_2S are described in the gas absorption literature (9-10). These include carbonates, organic amines, hydroxides, and inorganic salts.

Ethylene diamine $H_2N(CH_2)_2NH_2$, was chosen as the carrier to study the facilitated transport of H_2S in ion exchange membranes for several reasons. It can be singly protonated to produce a carrier which can then be exchanged into an ion exchange membrane to form the facilitated transport membrane. The mechanisms for the reactions of EDA with acid gases have been studied and some kinetic data exist as described below.

Gioia and Astarita (11) and Astarita (10) have reported that the reaction of H_2S with all bases in solution is a proton transfer reaction:

$$H_2S + B = BH^+ + HS^-. \tag{1}$$

These reactions are extremely fast with second order rate constants on the order of 10^{11} $M^{-1}s^{-1}$ (12). Astarita (10) assumes these reactions to be essentially instantaneous and, therefore, at equilibrium everywhere in the liquid phase. Consequently, there is considerable evidence to conclude that the reaction of H_2S with EDA^+ in solution is:

$$H_2S + H_2N(CH_2)_2NH_3^+ = HS^- + {}^+H_3N(CH_2)_2NH_3^+. \tag{2}$$

Structure of PFSA Cation Exchange Membranes. In the early 1970s a perfluorosulfonic acid ionomer was developed for use in electrochemical applications, especially the chloralkali process for the production of chlorine and caustic (13). The structure of these ionomers is shown in Figure 2. The acid form of the ionomer can be easily neutralized to cationic form by reaction with appropriate base such as NaOH. The mechanical, chemical, and ionic transport properties of these membranes have been extensively studied (14-16). Mathematical models of the transport of electrolytes through IEMs have been developed (17-18).

Data presented by these authors leads to a microstructure model of a fluorocarbon polymer backbone phase, polar ionic regions containing the sulfonate ions and the majority of the absorbed water, and an interfacial region between the polar ionic and nonpolar polymer phases (16). We are postulating that the facilitated transport of gas molecules occurs through the water containing ionic regions of the ionomer support.

Experimental Procedure

Flux Measurement. The apparatus and procedure used to measure membrane fluxes was described in detail by Bateman et al. (19) and Way (20). The flux measurement system consists of the gas flow system which delivers a gas mixture of known concentration to a membrane cell, a gas chromatograph with thermal conductivity detector for analysis of the feed and product side gas streams, and a computer for data acquisition and reduction. The gas streams were saturated with water upstream of the membrane cell. A cold trap removed the water prior to chromatographic analysis. All measurements were made

at ambient conditions of 298 K and 84.0 kPa. The chromatograph was
calibrated by injecting 1.0 cm³ aliquots of premixed gases of interest (1.0% in He).

Membrane Preparation. The ion exchange films (1100 g equivalent
molecular weight, 170 μm thickness) were obtained from the manufacturer in the acid form. The dry mass of the membranes was
determined and the number of ion exchange sites was calculated using
the equivalent molecular weight of the ionomer. The membranes were
converted to the Na salt form by soaking them in NaOH solutions
overnight. The amount of the NaOH used to prepare the solution was
at least 100 times the number of ion exchange sites available in the
membrane. The Na salt form was used as a nonreactive membrane for
measurements of the diffusive contributions of the individual gases
necessary to calculate the facilitation factor. After the transport
measurements were made, the Na membrane was converted to reactive
EDA salt form by soaking the membrane in an aqueous solution of EDA
overnight. A fifty-fold excess of EDA was used to obtain completed
exchange of the EDA for Na counterions. To create the monopositive
ion of EDA, one equivalent of HCl was added to the solution prior to
the exchange. The extent of exchange was measured by analysis of
the exchange solutions for Na by atomic emission spectroscopy. The
water content of the membranes at equilibrium was measured using the
gravimetric method of Yeager and Steck ($\underline{16}$). Table 1 presents the
results of the measurements. The water content of the EDA membranes
was used to calculate the effective concentrations of the EDA carrier species of 8.32 M. The thickness of the water swollen membranes
was 200 μm. Both Na and EDA form membranes were thoroughly rinsed
with distilled water prior to the mass transfer experiments.

Table 1. Water Content of Acid and Salt Form IEMs

| Sample | Water Content, cm³/g | | |
	H^+ Membrane	Na Membrane	EDA Membrane
1		0.18	0.10
2		0.17	0.12
3	0.25	0.17	
4	0.25	0.17	
5		0.18	0.11
Avg.	0.25	0.17	0.11

Results and Discussion

H_2S and H_2S/CH_4 Transport Data. Hydrogen sulfide fluxes were measured at ambient conditions (84.0 kPa, 298 K) for both Na and EDA
IEMs for feed mole fractions up to 0.05 H_2S. Figure 3 is a plot of
steady-state H_2S flux versus the log-mean mole fraction driving
force for both membranes. Each point is the average of at least
five steady-state flux values. Ninety-five percent confidence inter-
vals were less than 2% of the mean for the EDA IEM values and less
than 3.5% for the Na IEM values.

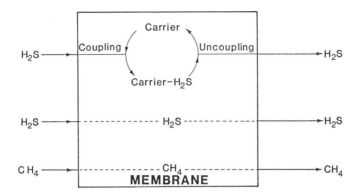

$$H_2S + Carrier \xrightleftharpoons[\text{Uncoupling}]{\text{Coupling}} Carrier - H_2S$$

Figure 1.   A schematic diagram of the facilitated transport process.

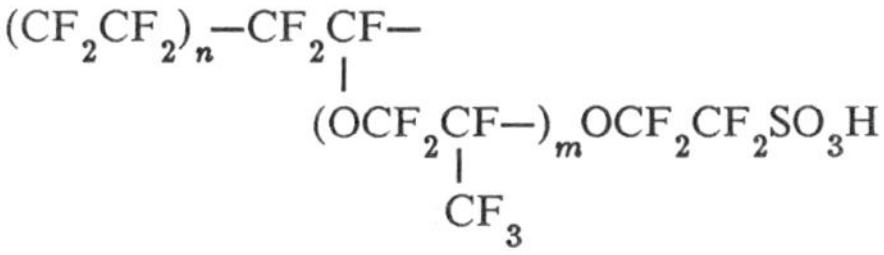

$$(CF_2CF_2)_n - CF_2CF-$$
$$(OCF_2CF-)_m OCF_2CF_2SO_3H$$
$$CF_3$$

Figure 2.   The structure of the perfluorosulfonic acid cation exchange membrane. The value of m=1 for membranes used in this study.

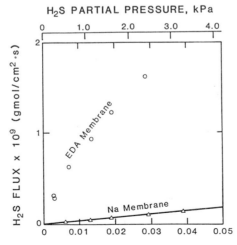

Figure 3.   The H_2S flux for both EDA and Na membranes as a function of log-mean mole fraction driving force.

The log-mean mole fraction was chosen as the best way to
describe the driving force for mass transfer. Since the membrane
cell is analogous to a flat plate, counterflow, heat exchanger, a
log- mean mole fraction difference, similar to a log-mean
temperature difference was defined as:

$$\Delta Y_{lm} = \frac{\left(y^i_f - y^o_s\right) - y^o_f}{\ln \left(\left(y^i_f - y^o_s\right)/y^o_f\right)} \qquad (3)$$

where

y^i_f = feed inlet mole fraction,
y^o_f = feed outlet mole fraction, and
y^o_s = sweep outlet mole fraction.

The permeability of a facilitated transport membrane is a function
of the H_2S partial pressure difference across the membrane. Consequently, use of the log-mean mole fraction difference accounts for
the changes observed in H_2S mole fraction between the inlet and outlet of the feed and sweep gas streams.

The H_2S flux data for the Na IEM in Figure 3 are a linear function of the Δy_{lm} driving force. Fluxes ranged from 2.68 x 10^{-11} to
1.38 x 10^{-10} gmol/(cm²·s). Low H_2S feed gas concentrations were
used for two reasons. A mixture of 5% H_2S in He was used as the
feed gas to reduce the amount of H_2S present in the laboratory.
This mixture was diluted with He to obtain feed mole fractions smaller than 0.05. Also, the majority of synthetic and natural gases
contain very small concentrations of H_2S. Therefore, small concentrations were necessary to collect data in the region of interest.
A least squares fit of the diffusive data yielded the following equation for the flux in gmol/(cm²·s) as a function of driving force,

$$N_{H_2S} = 3.62 \text{ x } 10^{-9} \Delta y_{lm}. \qquad (4)$$

The intercept of this equation was forced through the origin since
the diffusive flux must be zero at zero driving force. The fluxes
for the EDA IEM are an order of magnitude greater than the Na IEM
fluxes which clearly demonstrates the EDA facilitates the transport
of H_2S. Due to the low H_2S mole fractions in the feed gas, the facilitation factors are high, ranging from 15.8 to 26.4 for feed gases containing 5% to 1% H_2S, respectively. The carrier saturation
phenomena observed for facilitated transport of CO_2 in IEMs (6) and
ILMs (21) data are not observed in this case for H_2S probably because of the small feed gas mole fractions studied. The carrier
saturation problem will be discussed in more detail below.

It is assumed that equation 1 is the complexation reaction
which facilitates the transport of H_2S. However, it is difficult to
justify this reaction taking place within a PFSA membrane since the
anionic species HS^- is created and anions are excluded from the matrix by electrostatic repulsion. However, if the HS^- species and
the EDA^{2+} species exist as a ion pair having a +1 charge, then the
complexation reaction would not be hampered by unfavorable thermodynamics. Also, the reaction would conform to the A + B = AB reaction

mechanism used in many of the mathematical models of facilitated transport.

In order to clarify the complexation reaction mechanisms, H_2S transport experiments were performed using tetramethyl EDA [chemical formula $(CH_3)_2N(CH_2)_2N(CH_3)_2$] as a carrier in an IEM. The H_2S complexation reaction with EDA as well as most primary amines is postulated to be an acid base reaction (10). Since TMEDA is also a strong base, it should accept protons from the H_2S and act as a carrier in an IEM environment. A facilitation factor of 1.93 was measured for a TMEDA IEM at an H_2S feed mole fraction of 0.05. The degree of facilitation with the TMEDA membrane was much smaller than the EDA membrane ($F_{EDA}=15.8$), but the data for the TMEDA IEM does support the acid-base complexation mechanism for H_2S facilitated transport. The smaller F value for the TMEDA membrane may be due to the very low mobility of the TMEDA or because the binding between H_2S and TMEDA is so strong that the rate of the decomplexation reaction is very slow.

An alternate chemical mechanism for the H_2S transport data is that the HS^- species is the complex. Formed by reaction with the amine, HS^- could diffuse to the sweep side of the membrane where reaction with the EDA^{2+} species could produce H_2S and EDA. However, this explanation appears to be inconsistent with results using TMEDA as a carrier. If HS^- is the carrier species, then similar results might be expected for membranes incorporating either EDA and TMEDA carriers. However, the H_2S facilitation factor for the EDA IEM is 8.2 times larger than F for the TMEDA IEM. More research would help elucidate the chemical mechanism of H_2S facilitated transport in ionomers.

The maximum H_2S facilitated flux value corresponds to an H_2S permeability of 332×10^{-9} $cm^3(STP)cm/(cm^2 \cdot s \cdot kPa)$. Matson (8) reported a H_2S permeability range of $2250-3000 \times 10^{-9}$ $cm^3 \cdot cm/(cm^2 \cdot s \cdot kPa)$ for an ILM containing an aqueous solution of K_2CO_3 for a temperature range of 363-403 K. The feed gas H_2S partial pressure in Matson's studies was approximately 20 kPa with a total feed pressure of 2.17×10^3 kPa. Robb (22) reported an ambient temperature H_2S permeability of 638×10^{-9} $cm^3cm/(cm^2 \cdot s \cdot kPa)$ for a silicone rubber membrane. However, polymer membranes such as silicone rubber have much lower selectivities than facilitated transport membranes.

Figure 4 gives the results of the H_2S/CH_4 transport experiments using the same EDA IEM that was used for the single component H_2S experiments. The experiments were performed using a binary feed gas of H_2S/CH_4 and measuring the simultaneous flux of both components. The ratio of the steady-state H_2S flux to the steady-state CH_4 flux was plotted as a function of the log-mean driving forces of CH_4 and H_2S. Even at a very small H_2S driving force of 1.85×10^{-3} and a large CH_4 driving force of 0.898, the H_2S flux was 2.47 times the CH_4 flux. The flux ratio increases with increasing H_2S driving force and decreasing CH_4 driving force to a value of 55.7 for a CH_4 feed mole fraction of 0.2 and an H_2S feed mole fraction of 0.04. The facilitation factors range from 13.3 to 23.6 as the H_2S driving force decreases from 1.68×10^{-2} to 1.85×10^{-3}. The high facilitation factors help to explain the high selectivities of the EDA IEMs.

Converting the flux ratios to separation factors by normalizing the fluxes with the driving forces, separation factors of 792-1200 are obtained corresponding to flux ratios of 55.7 and 2.47, respectively. Kimura et al. (21) give H_2S/N_2 separation factors for several polymer membrane materials and the aqueous K_2CO_3 ILM first reported by Matson et al. (8). They claim that the N_2 permeability should be very similar to $\overline{CH_4}$. The separation factor (H_2S/N_2) for cellulose acetate was 12, 23 for silicone rubber, and over 1000 for the ILM. These polymer separation factors are good estimates of the selectivity of current commercial gas separation membranes such as cellulose ester hollow fiber modules and the silicone rubber/polysulfone hollow fiber modules for the H_2S/CH_4 separation. This comparison indicates that very high selectivities are obtainable with facilitated transport membranes and that the EDA IEM data are similar to previous ILM studies. Using an ion exchange membrane as a support for a facilitated transport membrane does not reduce the selectivity for acid gases over CH_4 when compared with an ILM configuration.

A consistency check on mixture transport experiments with one facilitated species and one or more species which do not react with the carrier is to plot the flux of the nonreacting permeate against the driving force. Figure 5 is a plot of CH_4 flux as a function of the log-mean mole fraction driving force for H_2S/CH_4 feed gases and for measurements of CH_4 flux measurements made for the same membrane. These points essentially lie on the same line as the points from H_2S/CH_4 experiments. One explanation is that the diffusing CH_4 molecule sees essentially the same environment in both the CH_4/He and the H_2S/CH_4 experiments.

Modeling and Analysis. The following equation has been derived for the facilitation factor F (23):

$$F = \frac{\left[1 + \frac{\alpha K}{1 + K}\right]\left[1 + \frac{2}{Sh}\right]}{1 - \frac{\alpha K}{1 + K}\left(\frac{\tanh \lambda}{\lambda}\right) + \left[1 + \frac{\alpha K}{1 + K}\right]\frac{2}{Sh}} \tag{5}$$

where

$$\alpha = \frac{D_{AB}C_T}{D_A C_{AO}} \tag{6}$$

$$K = K_{eq}C_{AO} \tag{7}$$

$$Sh = \frac{kL}{D_A} \tag{8}$$

$$\varepsilon = \frac{D_{AB}k_r}{L^2} \tag{9}$$

$$\lambda = \frac{1}{2}\left[\frac{1 + (\alpha+1)\,K}{\varepsilon\,(1+K)}\right]^{1/2} \tag{10}$$

Since the H_2S-EDA complexation reaction is very fast, the reaction can be assumed to be at equilibrium and the transport is limited by

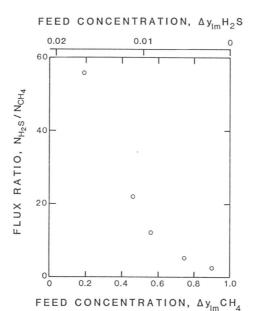

Figure 4.   The H_2S/CH_4 flux ratio as a function of feed gas mixture composition.

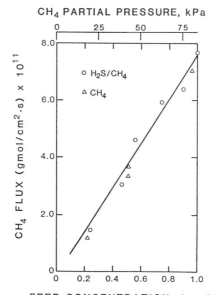

Figure 5.   The CH_4 fluxes for both H_2S/CH_4 and CH_4 transport experiments as a function of log-mean mole fraction driving force.

the diffusion rate. Under these conditions, $(\tanh \lambda)/\lambda$ approaches 0 and equation 5 can be recast in terms of E, the enhancement factor:

$$E^{-1} = (F-1)^{-1} = (1 + 2/Sh) \, \alpha^{-1} + 2/Sh[(\alpha K + 1)/(\alpha K)] + (\alpha K)^{-1} \qquad (11)$$

Since α^{-1} is directly proportional to C_{AO}, a plot of E^{-1} versus Δy_{lm} should produce a straight line if the reaction equilibrium assumption holds. Also, if $\alpha K \gg 1$, the intercept of this line is $2/Sh$ and it provides a measure of the external mass transfer resistance for the membrane. Figure 6 is a plot of E^{-1} for the H_2S transport data from Figure 3. The data plot as a straight line with an intercept of 3.63×10^{-2}. The correlation coefficient of the enhancement factor plot is 0.987. Therefore, the reaction equilibrium assumption is valid and external mass transfer resistances can be neglected.

The diffusivities in the IEM were calculated based on the volume of absorbed water. Based on the three phase model of PFSA membranes, the assumption was made that transport of the gas molecules, EDA, and complexed EDA occurs through the water containing regions of the ionomer. The diffusional path length was taken to be the swollen thickness of the membrane, 200 μm. An effective porosity, ϕ, of the Na IEM membrane was calculated to be 0.30 by dividing the volume of water absorbed by the total volume of the membrane. The calculated diffusion coefficient of H_2S in the Na IEM was corrected for the effective porosity.

The effective diffusivities for H_2S and the H_2S-EDA complex are needed to compute the mobility ratio α. The effective diffusivity of H_2S in the IEM was determined from the slope of the linear fit of the flux data for the Na membrane using the following equation:

$$D_A = \frac{\text{slope } L}{\phi \; C_{AO}} \qquad (12)$$

A value of 2.85×10^{-6} cm^2/s was obtained. The effective diffusion coefficient for the complex can be calculated from the slope of the enhancement factor plot in Figure 6 using the equation:

$$D_{AB} = \frac{D_A C_{AO}}{\text{slope } C_T} \qquad (13)$$

The effective diffusivity of the H_2S-EDA complex was 2.52×10^{-8} cm^2/s.

Literature values for the H_2S-EDA equilibrium constant in solution are unavailable. However, use of equilibrium constants for solution would probably result in poor agreement with the experimental data since reactions in PFSA membranes have been shown to have substantially different activation and rate parameters by Lieber and Lewis (24). However, the K_{eq} can be calculated from the intercept of the enhancement factor plot. Simplifying equation 11 and substituting the individual variables back into the dimensionless groups the following equation for the equilibrium constant is obtained:

$$K_{eq} = \frac{D_A}{D_{AB} C_T (\text{intercept of } E^{-1} \text{ plot})} \qquad (14)$$

The value is 374 M^{-1}.

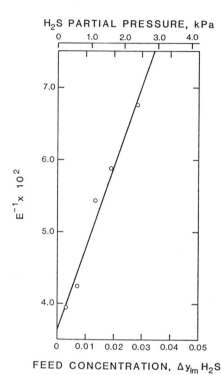

Figure 6. The inverse of the H_2S enhancement factor as a function of log-mean mole fraction driving force.

Once the properties of the system are known, equation 5 can be used to calculate facilitation factors which can be compared to the experimental data. The properties used in the calculation are summarized in Table 2.

Table 2. Property Values Used to Predict Facilitation Factors

Property	Value
Solute diffusivity	$2.85 \cdot 10^{-6}$ cm^2/s
Complex diffusivity	$2.52 \cdot 10^{-8}$ cm^2/s
Solubility in H$_2$O	$8.46 \cdot 10^{-2}$ M
Carrier concentration	8.32 M
Equilibrium constant	$3.74 \cdot 10^2$ M^{-1}
Forward rate constant	$1.0 \cdot 10^{11}$ M^{-1}s^{-1}
Reverse rate constant	$2.67 \cdot 10^8$ s^{-1}
Membrane thickness	0.02 cm

The comparison of predicted and experimental values for F is presented in Table 3.

Table 3. Comparison of Predicted Facilitation Factors
with Experimental Values

Δy_{1m}	F_{exp}	F_{model}
0.0029	26.4	26.2
0.00702	24.6	23.5
0.0133	19.4	20.4
0.0189	18.0	18.2
0.0284	15.8	15.5

The agreement is excellent. Since the equilibrium constant and the complex diffusivity were not independently measured, this approach is semiempirical, yet it is very valuable as it allows calculation of facilitation factors at conditions that were not studied experimentally.
    These predictions were made for 200 μm membranes. Industrial application of this technology will require the use of membranes which are two orders of magnitude thinner. In order to use the model to predict facilitation factors for thinner membranes, it is necessary to determine whether the reaction equilibrium assumption still applies. The parameter $(\tanh \lambda)/\lambda$ has a value of 0 if the system is diffusion limited and 1 if the facilitated transport system is reaction rate limited. At a thickness of 1μm, the value of $(\tanh \lambda)/\lambda$ is of the order 10^{-5}, which implies that the system is diffusion limited and that the simplified analytical model can be used to predict facilitation factors. If the solubility of H$_2$S, the pressure and temperature dependence of the equilibrium constant and the diffusion coefficients are known, then F could be estimated at industrial conditions.

Facilitated transport membranes are often subject to carrier saturation at high permeate partial pressure driving forces (6,20). This is a formidable impediment to industrial application of this technology. This phenomenon can be explained by examining the value of the dimensionless equilibrium constant $K = K_{eq}C_{AO}$. Kemena et al. (25) performed an optimization study and determined that the maximum facilitation occurs when $1 < K < 10$. If $K_{eq} \gg 1$, then good facilitation is only observed at low driving forces. At high partial pressure driving forces, when C_{AO} is large, the value of K is $\gg 1$, and little facilitation is observed. Consequently, this could be a problem at industrial conditions. The implications for H_2S facilitated transport in PFSA membranes are twofold to minimize carrier saturation. Operate the membrane at high total pressure and low H_2S partial pressure. H_2S is often present at low concentration in syngas from gasified coal and in natural gas. Another option may be to operate the membrane at atmospheric pressure and high H_2S mole fraction. This could be accomplished by running the facilitated transport membrane in series with a polymer membrane to process the permeate at ambient pressure analogous to physical and chemical absorption units in series. Recompression of the permeate after the first stage would be avoided which could improve overall process efficiency and economics.

Conclusions

This is the first study of H_2S facilitated transport of PFSA ionomers. Hydrogen sulfide and methane fluxes were measured at ambient conditions for 200 μm PFSA membranes containing monopositive EDA counterions as carriers. Facilitation factors up to 26.4 and separation factors for H_2S/CH_4 up to 1200 were observed. The H_2S transport is diffusion limited. The data were well represented by a simplified reaction equilibrium model. Calculation of dimensionless groups indicates that H_2S transport would be diffusion limited even at a membrane thickness of 1 μm.

Acknowledgments

The authors would like to acknowledge the support of the Dept. of Energy, Morgantown Energy Technology Center for this work under DOE Contract No. DE-AI21-84MC21271. Jenene F. Bewlay made the measurements of water absorption in ion exchange membranes. We would also like to thank Prof. Carl A. Koval of the University of Colorado Chemistry Dept. and Dr. Louis L. Burton and Dr. C.G. Michael Quah of The DuPont Co. for helpful discussions.

Nomenclature

C_{io} = concentration of species i at the feed gas/membrane interface
    = $y_i S_i$
C_i = concentration of species i
D_i = effective diffusion coefficient of species i in the membrane
E = enhancement factor = F - 1
F = facilitation factor, ratio of flux with carrier present to flux without carrier

K = dimensionless equilibrium constant
K_{eq} = equilibrium constant
L = membrane thickness
M = molarity, gmol/l
S_i = solubility of species i in water
k = mass transfer coefficient
k_f = forward rate constant
k_r = reverse rate constant
y_i = mole fraction of species i in the gas phase

Subscripts

A = permeating gas
B = carrier-gas complex
AB = carrier-gas complex
T = total amount of carrier
i = any species

Greek Letters

α = mobility ratio
ε = inverse Damkohler number
ϕ = effective membrane porosity

Literature Cited

1.   King, C. J., "Separation Processes Based on Reversible Chemical Complexation," Proceedings of the Joint Conference on Separation Processes, Taipei, Taiwan, 1983.
2.   Way, J. D.; Noble, R. D.; Flynn, T. M.; Sloan, E. D. J. Membr. Sci. 1982, 12, 239.
3.   Matson, S. L.; Lopez, J.; Quinn, J. L. Chem. Eng. Sci. 1983, 38, 503.
4.   Way, J. D.; Noble, R. D.; Bateman, B. R. In Materials Science of Synthetic Membranes; Lloyd, D. R., Ed.; ACS Symposium Series No. 269; American Chemical Society: Washington, DC, 1985; pp. 119-128.
5.   LeBlanc, O. G.; Ward, W. J.; Matson, S.L.; Kimura, S. G. J. Membr. Sci. 1980, 6, 339.
6.   Ward, W. J., "Immobilized Liquid Membranes," In Recent Developments in Separation Science, Li, N. N., Ed.; CRC Press: Cleveland, OH, 1972.
7.   Way, J. D.; Noble, R. D.; Reed, D. L.; Ginley, G. M.; Jarr, L. A. AIChE J. 1987, 33, in press.
8.   Matson, S. L.; Herrick, C. S.; Ward, W. J. Ind. Eng. Chem., Process Des. Dev. 1977, 16, 370.
9.   Kohl, A. L.; Riesenfeld, F. C. Gas Purification; Gulf: Houston, TX, 1979.
10. Astarita, g.; Savage, D. W.; Bisio, A. Gas Treating with Chemical Solvents; Wiley: New York, 1983.
11. Gioia, F.; Astarita, G. Ind. Eng. Chem. Fund. 1967, 6, 370.
12. Eigen, H. Suomen Kemistilehti 1961, A34, 416.

13. Leitz, F. B.; Accomazzo, M. A.; Michalek S. A. Proc. 141st National Meeting of the Electrochemical Society, Houston, TX, 1972.

14. Grot, W. G. F.; Munn, G. E.; Walnsley, P. N. Proc. 141st National Meeting of the Electrochemical Society, Houston, TX, 1972.

15. Yeo, S. C.; Eisenberg, A. J. Appl. Polymer Sci. 1977, 21, 875.

16. Yeager, H. L.; Steck, A. J. Electrochem. Soc. 1982, 129, 328.

17. Gierke, T. D. Proc. Electrochemical Society Meeting, Atlanta, GA, 1977.

18. Pintauro, P. N.; Bennion, D. N. Ind. Eng. Chem. Fund. 1984, 23, 230.

19. Bateman, B. R.; Way, J. D.; Larson, K. M. Sep Sci. Tech. 1984, 19, 21.

20. Way, J. D. Ph.D. Thesis, University of Colorado, Boulder, CO, 1986.

21. Kimura, S. G.; Matson, S. L.; Ward, W. J. III In Recent Developments in Separation Science, Li, N. N., Ed.; CRC Press, Cleveland, OH, 1979.

22. Robb, W. L. Ann. N. Y. Acad. Sci. 1967, 146, 119.

23. Noble, R. D.; Way, J. D.; Powers, L. A. Ind. Eng. Chem. Fund. 1986, 25, 450.

24. Lieber, C. M.; Lewis, N. S. J. Am. Chem. Soc. 1985, 107, 7190.

25. Kemena, L. L.; Noble, R. D.; Kemp, N. J. J. Membr. Sci. 1983, 15, 259.

RECEIVED January 9, 1987

Chapter 10

Gas Permeation and Separation with Aqueous Membranes Immobilized in Microporous Hydrophobic Hollow Fibers

Ramesh R. Bhave[1] and Kamalesh K. Sirkar

Department of Chemistry and Chemical Engineering, Stevens Institute of Technology, Castle Point, Hoboken, NJ 07030

A simple immobilized liquid membrane (ILM) structure obtained by immobilizing aqueous solutions in microporous hydrophobic Celgard X-10 hollow fibers has been utilized for gas permeation and separation. Permeation of pure N_2 through pure water immobilized in the fiber has been employed to characterize the microporous hollow fiber by determining its tortuosity factor. Studies on separating a CO_2-N_2 mixture have been conducted with pure water and an aqueous 30% wt/wt K_2CO_3 ILM-s at applied pressure differences up to 550 cm Hg. Gas separation was studied in two modes: high pressure feed through fiber lumina; high pressure feed on the permeator shell side. In both modes of operation, no effect of any possible fiber deformation was observed on gas permeation and separation. For separation of the CO_2-N_2 mixture, the aqueous 30% wt/wt K_2CO_3 ILM-s were found to be quite efficient and stable for extended periods of operation.

Synthetic polymeric membranes are often used in industrial practice for the separation of gas mixtures (1-2). For instance, recovery of hydrogen from purge gas streams containing CO_2, CO, CH_4 etc., recovery of CO_2 from mixed well head-gases in enhanced oil recovery applications, separation of atmospheric air etc. are now carried out in permeators using synthetic polymeric membranes (2). Gas separation by synthetic polymeric membranes, however, suffers from low values of flux levels and selectivity achievable for a given separation. Very thin membranes are needed to produce industrially acceptable flux levels since the diffusivity of most gases in polymers is quite low. The magnitude of separation factors obtained are also usually not very high (3-5) unless the mixture components are radically different.

[1]Current address: ALCOA, Alcoa Technical Center, Alcoa Center, PA 15069

0097-6156/87/0347-0138$06.00/0
© 1987 American Chemical Society

An alternative approach to developing high performance membranes is to utilize liquids immobilized in microporous polymeric supports as membrane materials. Immobilized liquid membranes (ILM-s) containing substances which chemically augment or facilitate the transport of one component across the membrane can often achieve gas separation with high selectivity (4-9). Conventional ILM techniques (such as that employed by GE workers (7-8)) utilize highly porous hydrophilic supports such as cellulose acetate, regenerated cellulose to immobilize aqueous electrolytic solutions (4,7,10). For applications having positive applied pressure differences the same group had employed these hydrophilic supports that were backed up by a microporous hydrophobic membrane of very small pore size (e.g. Celgard polypropylene film, Goretex teflon film, etc.) to prevent liquid expulsion (7,11).

We have, however, adopted a simpler structure by utilizing microporous hydrophobic Celgard supports for liquid immobilization. This method of supporting aqueous ILM-s is also less susceptible to membrane flooding by moisture condensation. With the help of an exchange process, we have immobilized water or aqueous electrolyte solutions in microporous hydrophobic Celgard films and hollow fibers (12-13). Gas separation with such ILM-s was found to be quite stable and efficient over a wide range of conditions, including high ΔP values (12-13).

Thus, the major difference between our ILM structure to that utilized by previous workers lies in the fact that we have a single-ply structure wherein the liquid membrane is immobilized within the pores of a microporous hydrophobic support as compared to the two-ply structure of GE workers discussed above. To be noted also is that moisture condensation on the hydrophobic supports does not automatically lead to flooding due to the hydrophobic nature of the surface (unlike that with hydrophilic membranes).

Hollow fibers rather than flat membranes are often the preferred support form for practical gas separation due to the high membrane surface area that can be packed in a permeator and their high pressure capability. In the earlier study (13) the hydrophobic microporous polypropylene hollow fiber support used was Celgard X-20. Due to its dimensions and porosity it could not be operated at positive shell side ΔP value beyond 282 cm Hg as significant compressive deformation as observed. We have utilized in this study Celgard X-10 hollow fibers. These fibers having a lower porosity and much smaller dimensions can withstand much greater applied pressures whether applied on the outside or on the inside of the fiber. The performance of such a simple ILM structure is the subject at hand.

This paper describes pure N_2 permeation and CO_2-N_2 separation characteristics of ILM-s of pure water and aqueous 30% wt/wt K_2CO_3 solutions immobilized in Celgard X-10 hollow fibers. Measurements were carried out over a wide range of applied pressure differences. The CO_2 partial pressure difference was varied from about 40 cm Hg to 140 cm Hg while the N_2 partial pressure difference was increased from about 125 cm Hg to 425 cm Hg. The total applied pressure difference was varied between 140 to 550 cm Hg. Facilitated transport membranes of aqueous 30% wt/wt K_2CO_3 solution for the separation of CO_2 from N_2 were utilized and the separation behaviors

were investigated in two operational modes. The first mode had the
feed gas flowing through the fiber lumen; in the second mode, the
feed gas flowed over the fiber outside surface.

ILM Strategies

Several strategies for utilization of ILM-s for gas separation purposes have been reported in the literature. It is useful to briefly
review the salient features of the various ILM approaches adopted for
gas permeation and separation.
        Matson et.al.(14), Kimura and Walmet (11) and other GE investi-
gators employed a two-ply structure wherein a highly porous hydrophilic support was spontaneously wetted by the aqueous liquid and
then backed up by a very fine pore size microporous hydrophobic membrane for high ΔP applications (up to 20 atmospheres). Ward and Robb
(8) had used a thin silicone rubber membrane on the downstream side
instead of a microporous hydrophobic membrane. Ward (15-16), Otto
and Quinn (17) and Donaldson and Quinn (18) have reported facilitated
transport gas flux measurements through a liquid layer immobilized
between two thin highly permeable polymeric films of silicone (or
silicone copolymers). These authors carried out their investigations
under atmospheric pressure conditions on both side of the ILM. The
same strategy was followed by Suchdeo and Schultz (10).
        Anisotropic cellulose ester fibers (useful for reverse osmosis)
with a dense skin and porous substructure were employed as supports
for immobilizing aqueous $AgNO_3$ solutions for separating olefins from
paraffins (6). However, these authors did not operate under any
significant ΔP conditions, primarily to reduce membrane liquid loss
under positive applied pressure differential.
        No positive ΔP values were also used by Bateman et.al. (19) who
incorporated a polar organic liquid (viz. formamide) inside the pores
of hydrophobic microporous Celgard 2500 film wetted first by a surfactant solution. We have similarly studied Celgard 3500 films;
aqueous solutions were easily incorporated since Celgard 3500 films
were treated with surfactants (20). However, the stability and re-
producibility were found to be poor. The rewetting characteristics
of Celgard 3500 films with surfactant depletion (due to washing,
re-exchange with aqueous solution, etc.) were found to be less than
satisfactory.
        The usefulness of employing ILM-s for gas separation arising
primarily from their ability to yield high values of selectivity and
permeability is well known. Unfortunately, the practical application
of ILM-s to gas separations is often hindered by lack of long term
stability unless the atmospheric humidity is very well controlled.
Recently, Deetz and Zook (21) have shown that stabilization of the
liquid phase can be achieved by immobilizing the liquid in pores
small enough to significantly reduce the molar free energy of the
solution via the Kelvin effect. As a result, such membranes can
handle much wider humidity excursions and can be easily rewetted.
These authors utilized anisotropic porous polymer supports (e.g.
cellulose acetate) for liquid immobilization (e.g. propylene carbonate, glycerol) and have demonstrated that, by using such stabi-
zied ultrathin liquid membranes, high fluxes at very low concentra-

tion gradients can be obtained. The use of ion exchange membranes to these ends by Le Blanc et al. (22) is also worthy of attention.

Experimental

The sweep gas method of Pye et al. (23) was utilized as described earlier (12) to measure the permeation rate of each feed gas species from a 100% relative humidity high pressure feed gas stream into a completely humidified sweep gas stream of pure helium at near atmospheric pressure. For details, the reader is referred to our previous work (12).

Apparatus

Hollow Fiber Permeator

Celgard X-10 microporous hollow fiber permeators were prepared by employing the following procedure. Permeators were constructed with 20 Celgard X-10 fibers of desired lengths (31.1 cm) by placing these in a 1/4 inch stainless steel tube equipped with 1/4 inch Swagelok end connections and by potting each fiber end into each tube end with a two-component epoxy resin. The two-component Armstrong epoxy resin was of the type C4-D and was obtained from Beacon Chemical Company, Mount Vernon, New York. Sufficient time (usually 24 hours) was allowed for complete curing of the epoxy resin before any gas permeation measurements.

Materials

Celgard X-10 hollow fibers were provided by Celgard Business Unit, Charlotte, North Carolina. These were of 150 μm O.D. and 100 μm I.D. with an average pore size of 0.03 μm. The membrane porosity was 0.02. The external membrane surface area available for permeation was 29.31 cm^2,
Potassium carbonate (K_2CO_3) of purity greater than 99% was obtained from Aldrich Chemical Company, Milwaukee, Wisconsin. Aqueous solutions of K_2CO_3 were prepared with distilled water.
Pure nitrogen (of at least 99.99% purity) was obtained from Matheson (East Rutherford, New Jersey). A primary standard CO_2-N_2 mixture of 25% CO_2 balance 75% N_2 was obtained from Matheson. Helium (99.99% pure) obtained from Matheson was employed as the sweep gas in the gas permeability apparatus. Helium (99.99% pure) was the carrier gas in the Varian 1420 Gas Chromatograph (GC) having a thermal conductivity detector (TCD) and a gas sampling valve (GSV). A series of primary standard gas mixtures containing CO_2, N_2 or both with helium as the diluent were utilized to calibrate the GC.

Exchange Procedures for Immobilization of Aqueous Liquid Membrane in Hydrophobic Hollow Fibers

Figure 1 shows the schematic of the apparatus employed for the preparation of aqueous ILM-s in microporous Celgard hydrophobic hollow fibers. Pure water was first incorporated in the pores of the microporous Celgard X-10 hollow fiber supports all across the

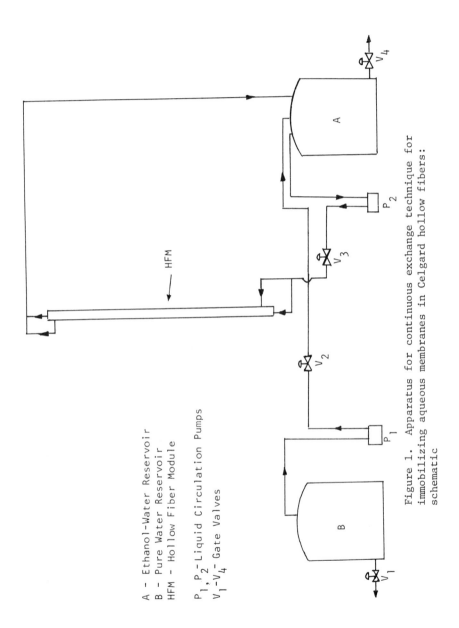

A – Ethanol-Water Reservoir
B – Pure Water Reservoir
HFM – Hollow Fiber Module

P_1, P_2- Liquid Circulation Pumps
V_1-V_4- Gate Valves

Figure 1. Apparatus for continuous exchange technique for
immobilizing aqueous membranes in Celgard hollow fibers:
schematic

thickness in a manner somewhat analogous to that described in detail in (12) for flat films. This procedure consisted of the following steps:

1. Aqueous 40% vol/vol ethanol stored in reservoir (A) was pumped into the shell and tube side of the hollow fiber module at a sufficiently high flow rate (>200 cm^3/min). This solution completely wetted the fibers. Thus a 40% aqueous ethanol solution was incorporated in the pores of the Celgard hollow fibers.

2. Next, pure water stored in a separate reservoir (B) was pumped into reservoir (A) at a very low flow rate ($\sim$50 cm^3/min) in a continuous manner. Thus the concentration of ethyl alcohol in reservoir (A) was continuously and gradually reduced from about 40% vol/vol to almost pure water.

3. The contents of reservoir (A) of decreasing ethanol concentration were simultaneously and continuously fed to the shell side and feed side of the module at sufficiently high flow rates. This procedure was followed till all ethanol in the fiber pores was replaced by pure water. The total time required for this process was about 3-4 hours. After such a condition was reached the rate of N$_2$ permeation through the ILM-s was determined and found to be constant, independent of the length of further exchange time.

For incorporating aqueous K$_2$CO$_3$ solution in the fiber pores, we started with fibers contianing pure water in the pores. Aqueous K$_2$CO$_3$ ILM-s were obtained by replacing pure water in the pores of Celgard X-10 hollow fibers by contacting with aqueous 30% wt/wt K$_2$CO$_3$ solution for several hours.

Experimental Procedure for Gas Permeation and/or Separation

The experimental procedure for permeation studies with hollow fiber modules was identical to that described by Bhave and Sirkar (12) for flat Celgard films except that the flat film test cell was replaced by the hollow fiber module (see Figure 1 in reference (12)).

Two modes of permeator operation were utilized. The first utilized feed gas on the tube side, while humidified helium flowing through the shell side, constituted the sweep gas. In the second mode of operation humidified sweep helium gas was introduced through the fiber lumen as the feed gas flowed on the shell side. The flow pattern was countercurrent in each case.

The flow rates of the completely humidified streams of feed and sweep were adjusted to the desired values. The flow rates of the high pressure feed gas were in the range of 15-25 cm^3/min whereas a sweep gas flow rate in the range of 6-15 cm^3/min was used at near atmospheric pressure.

After each experiment was concluded, the flow rates of all gas streams were brought to zero and the system was depressurized. The module was removed and re-exchanged with water or aqueous K$_2$CO$_3$ solution (as described earlier) depending on the type of ILM required in the subsequent experiment. Each measurement reported here was at least duplicated. The experimental data could be reproduced quite well. All measurements were done at room temperature ($\sim$24°C).

Analysis

The concentration of N_2 and CO_2 permeating from the feed side through
the liquid membrane into the sweep helium stream was determined with
the help of Varian 1420 Gas Chromatograph. Further details of the
analytical technique are available in (12).

Results and Discussion

The knowledge of tortuosity factor of the microporous hollow fibers
used in this study is important for characterizing   the gas permeation rate through the immobilized liquid membrane. Since it is not
available, an independent estimate was developed. We first consider
these results.
        The tortuosity factor for Celgard X-10 hollow fibers was esti-
mated at different values of applied pure N_2 pressure by studying
pure N_2 permeation across pure water immobilized in the pores of
the microporous hydrophobic Celgard support. Pure N_2 feed was introduced on the shell side whereas pure helium flowing through the
inside of the fiber lumen constituted the sweep gas. The following
equation can be used to obtain the tortuosity estimates, if Q_{N_2} is
known (10,12):

$$\tau = \frac{Q_{N_2} \times \epsilon \times \Delta P_{N_2} \times A}{R_{N_2} \times t_M} \tag{1}$$

        Table I reports the tortuosity factors for Celgard X-10 hollow
fibers. It can be seen that the value of τ varied from 3.59 to
4.34 when the value of applied ΔP_{N_2} was varied in the range of 140
to 444 cm Hg.
        In a recent investigation (13) we have reported the tortosity
factors for Celgard X-20 hollow fibers. The values of τ for
Celgard X-20 hollow fibers were found to vary from 2.27 to 3.26 when
the applied ΔP_{N_2} values were increased from 115 to 282 cm Hg. Thus
it can be seen that the tortuosity factor estimates for Celgard X-10
hollow fibers are significantly higher than those reported for
Celgard X-20 fibers. This can be expected since the porosity of
Celgard X-10 hollow fibers is considerably lower (0.2 vs. 0.4 for
Celgard X-20 fibers) and the operating pressures were considerably
higher. However, the capability of Celgard X-10 fibers to withstand
higher values of applied pressure without significant fiber deformation was found to be markedly superior to Celgard X-20 hollow fibers.
In the case of Celgard X-20 hollow fibers significant fiber deformation was observed (13) at applied ΔP values as low as 280 cm Hg,
whereas no significant effect of any fiber deformation was observed
at externally applied pressures up to 450 cm Hg. Under internally
pressurized conditions, we have also been able to operate at applied
pressure differences up to 550 cm Hg without fiber rupture and/or
leakage. This demonstrates the high pressure capability of smaller
microporous hydrophobic hollow fibers for immobilizing liquids.
        The value of gas permeability in reactive solutions such as
aqueous K_2CO_3 may be directly determined from Equation 1, as we can

Table I.   Estimated Tortuosity Factor for Celgard
X-10 Hollow Fibers

Partial pressure difference, N_2* cm Hg	N_2 permeation rate $X_3 10^3$ std cm^3/sec	Q_{N_2} X 10^9 $\dfrac{\text{std cm}^3(\text{cm})}{\text{cm}^2\text{sec-cm-Hg}}$	τ
140.37	0.53	5.87	3.59
217.42	0.79	5.83	3.70
289.88	1.04	5.78	3.72
341.19	1.16	5.75	3.90
393.10	1.24	5.70	4.17
444.79	1.34	5.67	4.34

No. of fibers = 20; Effective fiber length = 31.1 cm;
A = 29.31 cm^2; ε = 0.2; t_m = 2.54 X 10^{-3} cm.
* It is essentially equal to feed N_2 pressure since N_2 partial
pressure in helium is negligible.

use the τ value obtained with ILM-s of pure water. However, the value of gas permeability usually depends on both the partial pressure difference and the electrolyte concentration. For N_2, however, at a fixed aqueous K_2CO_3 concentration, the variation of Q_{N_2} with ΔP_{N_2} is very nominal. We have, therefore, used the pure N_2 water tortuosity values corresponding to a length-averaged value of ΔP_{N_2} along the permeator for reactive liquid membrane systems.

Separation of CO_2-N_2 Mixture

Pure Water ILM-s in Celgard X-10 Hollow Fibers

The separation of a CO_2-N_2 mixture consisting of 25% CO_2 and 75% N_2 through pure water immobilized in the pores of Celgard X-10 fibers all across its thickness was investigated at various applied pressure differences in the range of 235 to 437 cm Hg. The high pressure CO_2-N_2 feed gas was introduced on the shell side whereas pure helium sweep flowed through the fiber lumen. The results of these measurements are reported in Table II.

The CO_2-N_2 separation factor reported in Tables II and III has been defined as

$$\alpha_{CO_2-N_2} = Q_{CO_2}/Q_{N_2} = \frac{R_{CO_2}/\Delta P_{CO_2}}{R_{N_2}/\Delta P_{N_2}} \tag{2}$$

The experimental determination of $\alpha_{CO_2-N_2}$ requires measuring the CO_2 and N_2 permeation rates through an ILM of pure water or aqueous K_2CO_3 solution (as discussed in the next section) in the microporous hydrophobic Celgard X-10 support, at the desired applied ΔP_{CO_2} and ΔP_{N_2} values, respectively.

The data in Table II indicate that the permeation rate per unit partial pressure difference, $R_i/\Delta P_i$, for both CO_2 and N_2 remained substantially constant even though ΔP_{CO_2} and ΔP_{N_2} varied over a wide range. This result is similar to that reported in our earlier investigations with Celgard 2400 flat films (12) and Celgard X-20 hollow fibers (13). The CO_2 partial pressure was varied in the range of about 56 to 103 cm Hg while the N_2 partial pressure was increased from about 179 to 334 cm Hg. The CO_2-N_2 separation factor through pure water ILM-s in Celgard X-10 fibers was found to be in the range of 30-35, which is consistent with the range of values obtained in our other investigations (12-13) with pure water ILM-s in Celgard supports. The Q_{CO_2} values through water-filled ILM-s reported in Table II are also in agreement with values reported elsewhere in the literature (8).

It may also be determined from Table II that the fraction of feed gas permeated and the amounts of CO_2 and N_2 permeated in the pure helium sweep were very low (about 1-3%). Thus our calculations based on length-averaged ΔP_{CO_2} and ΔP_{N_2} do not vitiate the underlying principle of the permeability measurement technique (23).

Table II. CO_2-N_2 Separation Behavior through Pure Water ILM-s in Celgard X-10 Hollow Fibers*

ΔP_{CO_2} cm Hg	ΔP_{N_2} cm Hg	R_{CO_2} X 10^4 $\dfrac{std\ cm^3}{sec}$	R_{N_2} X 10^4 $\dfrac{std\ cm^3}{sec}$	$\dfrac{R_{CO_2}\ X\ 10^4}{\Delta P_{CO_2}}$ $\dfrac{std\ cm^3}{sec-cm\ Hg}$	$\dfrac{R_{N_2}\ X\ 10^7}{\Delta P_{N_2}}$ $\dfrac{std\ cm^3}{sec-cm\ Hg}$	Q_{N_2} X 10^9 $\dfrac{std\ cm^3\ (cm)}{cm^2-sec-cm\ Hg}$	Separation factor $\dfrac{Q_{CO_2}}{Q_{N_2}}$	Q_{CO_2} X 10^9 $\dfrac{std\ cm^3\ (cm)}{cm^2-sec-cm\ Hg}$
56.71	178.8	43.7	3.85	0.77	21.52	5.85	35.78	209.31
68.52	217.6	53.7	4.95	0.78	22.75	5.83	34.29	199.91
80.33	256.7	61.6	5.83	0.77	22.71	5.81	33.91	197.02
91.23	295.0	63.4	6.36	0.70	21.56	5.80	32.47	188.33
102.69	334.2	69.3	7.48	0.68	22.38	5.79	30.38	175.9

*Feed on the outside of the fiber lumen.
No. of fibers = 20; ε = 0.2 ; t_m = 2.54 X 10^{-3} cm;
A = 29.31 cm^2; Effective fiber length = 31.1 cm.

Aqueous 30% wt/wt K_2CO_3 ILM-s. The study of CO_2-N_2 mixture separation through aqueous K_2CO_3 ILM-s in Celgard X-10 hollow fibers was
carried out by utilizing two modes of permeator operation.

Feed through Inside of the Fiber Lumen. Table III (Set A) gives the
experimentally observed separation factor, $\alpha_{CO_2-N_2}$, for the CO_2-N_2
system with aqueous 30% wt/wt K_2CO_3 ILM-s at various total
feed gas pressures. These measurements were made with feed gas of
25% CO_2 and 75% N_2 through the inside of the fiber lumen. It can be
seen that the CO_2-N_2 separation factor with aqueous 30% wt/wt
K_2CO_3 ILM-s (I = 8.7 gion/liter) is several fold higher compared to
that with pure water ILM-s (I = 0). It is well known that the CO_2
transport rate through aqueous K_2CO_3 solutions can be substantially
augmented due to the reversible hydration reaction (6-7).

$$CO_2 + OH^- \xrightarrow[k_{-2}]{k_2} HCO_3^- \qquad (3)$$

In the case of CO_2-N_2 mixture, the reduction in the CO_2 permeability in the presence of salt is less prominent due to CO_2
facilitation discussed above, whereas the N_2 permeability is
substantially lowered ("salting-out" effect) in the aqueous 30%
wt/wt K_2CO_3 solution.

The effect of applied CO_2 partial pressure difference on the
separation factor was studied by varying the values of average ΔP_{CO_2}
in the range of about 43 cm Hg to about 133 cm Hg. The results
of these experiments are reported in Table III (Set A). It is evi-
dent that the value of $\alpha_{CO_2-N_2}$ at the lowest ΔP_{CO_2} (∿43 cm Hg) used
in this work is significantly higher than that obtained at the
relatively high value of ΔP_{CO_2} of around 130 cm Hg. Kimura et al. (7),
Kimura and Walmet (11) and other investigators (14) have also reported that in facilitated transport systems, Q_{CO_2} values were found to
increase as ΔP_{CO_2} was lowered. This is probably due to the fact that
when ΔP_{CO_2} values are low, the system belongs to the chemical
reaction rate controlled regime and, therefore, a decrease in ΔP_{CO_2}
leads to a higher rate and significant facilitation.

The data of Table III (Set A) also demonstrate the high pressure capability of Celgard X-10 hollow fibers. The CO_2-N_2 mixture
separation with aqueous 30% wt/wt K_2CO_3 ILM-s in Celgard X-10
fibers was studied at applied ΔP values up to about 550 cm Hg without
any significant effect on permeation due to any fiber deformation.
The values of stage cut and the ratio of amount of feed permeated to
sweep flow rate were quite low in the range of about 1-2% and 1-3%,
respectively. Thus, the basis for permeability measurement was not
affected. To demonstrate the stability of aqueous 30% wt/wt K_2CO_3
ILM-s in Celgard X-10 fibers, a few experiments were also
carried out for durations of up to 72 hours.

Feed on the Outside of the Fiber Lumen. Additional permeation and
CO_2-N_2 separation measurements were also carried out with aqueous
30% wt/wt K_2CO_3 ILM-s in Celgard X-10 by employing feed on the
outside of fibers and sweep through the fiber lumen. These are
reported in Table III (Set B). In this mode of permeator operation,

Table III. CO_2-N_2 Separation Behavior through 30% wt/wt Aqueous K_2CO_3 ILM-s in Celgard X-10 Hollow Fibers

ΔP_{CO_2} cm Hg	ΔP_{N_2} cm Hg	$R_{CO_2} \times 10^4$ $\dfrac{std\ cm^3}{sec}$	$R_{N_2} \times 10^4$ $\dfrac{std\ cm^3}{sec}$	Stage cut$^\Delta$ x 100	Feed permeated* $\overline{\text{Sweep flowrate}}$ X 100	$Q_{N_2} \times 10^9$ $\dfrac{std\ cm^3(cm)}{cm^2-sec-cmHg}$	Separation factor = $\dfrac{Q_{CO_2}}{Q_{N_2}}$	$Q_{CO_2} \times 10^9$ $\dfrac{std\ cm^3(cm)}{cm^2-sec-cmHg}$
A - Feed through inside of the fiber lumen								
43.4	134.55	24.1	0.5	0.86	1.36	0.67	150.9	101.13
75.69	236.96	38.6	0.93	1.58	2.54	0.64	130.1	83.26
93.33	291.76	38.7	1.05	1.59	2.46	0.64	116.7	74.69
111.7	350.77	44.1	1.25	1.83	2.90	0.63	111.1	69.98
132.8	412.27	51.1	1.53	1.27	3.26	0.62	105.4	65.29
B - Feed on the outside of the fiber lumen								
52.7	164.6	32.3	0.73	1.34	2.04	0.66	138.2	91.21
77.67	242.89	37.6	0.97	1.56	2.4	0.64	121.4	77.70

$^\Delta$Stage cut = (Amount of feed permeated/Feed in)

* (Amount of feed permeated/Total sweep out) x 100

No. of fibers = 20; ε = 0.2 ; Effective fiber length = 31.1 cm;

A = 29.31 cm^2 (feed on outside) ; A = 19.54 cm^2 (feed through the inside)

CO_2-N_2 separation characteristics were similar to those obtained with permeator operation mode where feed was passed through the fiber lumen.

Thus, it may be observed that aqueous ILM-s in microporous hydrophobic Celgard X-10 hollow fibers can perform gas separation in a stable and efficient manner at substantially high applied ΔP-s.

Comparison of Permeation Parameters: Immobilized Hollow Fiber Liquid Membranes vs. Nonporous Polymeric Hollow Fiber Membranes

Kulkarni et al. (3) have reported an estimate of $(P_{CO2})_{eff}/t_{eff}$ for Monsanto's Prism membranes. Their value is 41.7×10^{-6} std cm^3/cm^2-sec-cm Hg. For the present study, the corresponding value is 4.59×10^{-6} with pure water ILM-s and 2.22×10^{-6} with 30% wt/wt aqueous K_2CO_3 ILM-s. The porosity of X-10 hollow fibers used is only 0.2 and the tortuosity factor is correspondingly higher at 3.59 compared to X-20 fibers ($\epsilon = 0.40$, $\tau \approx 2.27$, (13)). Therefore, if smaller diameter X-20 fibers were available, the $(P_{CO_2})_{eff}/t_{eff}$ value could be raised by about 3.5 times.

Thus, with a more rigid support material of higher porosity (for example, cellulose acetate based ILM-s are highly porous with porosities in the range 70-80% and fiber dimensions corresponding to X-10 hollow fibers (O.D = 150 μm) the CO_2 permeabilities of these liquid membranes would be close to that of Monsanto membranes. However, separation factor with aqueous 30% wt/wt K_2CO_3 ILM-s will continue to be at least 6-7 times larger than that with nonporous polymeric hollow fiber membranes (at low values of ΔP_{CO_2}, an order of magnitude higher (13)).

Conclusions

Gas permeation and CO_2-N_2 mixture separation through aqueous membranes immobilized in the pores of microporous hydrophobic Celgard X-10 hollow fibers was carried out over a wide range of applied ΔP-s up to 550 cm Hg. Pure N_2 permeation through ILM-s of pure water in Celgard X-10 fibers was utilized to characterize the microporous hydrophobic support through the determination of the tortuosity factor. The high pressure capability of Celgard X-10 fibers under both external and internal pressurization has been demonstrated. Aqueous 30% wt/wt K_2CO_3 ILM-s were found to be efficient for CO_2-N_2 mixture separation and gave stable performances over extended periods of time.

Legend of Symbols

A   area available for gas permeation, cm^2
I   ionic strength of aqueous K_2CO_3 solution, gion/liter
k_2 second order forward reaction rate constant in Equation 3, cm^3/gmole-sec
k_{-2} second order backward reaction rate constant, cm^3/gmole-sec
Q_i permeability of the gaseous species, i through the ILM, std cm^3 (cm)/cm^2-sec-cm Hg.
ΔP_i partial pressure difference across the liquid membrane for the permeating species i, cm Hg

R_i permeation rate of the gaseous species i through the ILM, std cm^3/sec

t_M thickness of the microporous Celgard support, cm

Greek Letters

ε membrane porosity

τ tortuosity factor, Equation 1

$\alpha_{CO_2-N_2}$ separation factor, CO_2-N_2 system, Equation 2

Literature Cited

1. MacLean, D.L.; Graham, T.E. Chem. Engg. 1980, 87 (4), 54-55.
2. Parkinson, G. Chem. Engg. 1984, 91 (8), 14-19.
3. Kulkarni, S.S.; Funk, E.W.; Li, N.N.; Riley, R.L. AIChE Symps. Ser. 1983, 79 (229), 172-177.
4. Matson, S.L.; Lopez, J.; Quinn, J.A. Chem. Engng Sci. 1983, 38, 503-524.
5. Sengupta, A.; Sirkar, K.K. In Progress in Filtration and Separation; Wakeman, R.J., Ed.; Elsevier, Amsterdam, 1986; Vol. 4, 289-416.
6. Hughes, R.D.; Mahoney, J.A.; Steigelmann, E.F. In Recent Developments in Separation Science; Li, N.N.; Calo, J.M., Eds; CRC Press: Boca Raton, Florida, 1986; Vol. 9, 174-195.
7. Kimura, S.G.; Matson, S.L.; Ward, W.J. In Recent Developments in Separation Science; Li, N.N.; Ed.; CRC Press: West Palm Beach. Florida, 1979; Vol. 5, 11-25.
8. Ward, W.J.; Robb, W.L. Science 1967, 156, 1481-1484.
9. Way, J.D.; Noble, R.D.; Flynn, T.M.; Sloan, E.D. J. Membrane Sci. 1982, 12, 239-259.
10. Suchdeo, S.R.; Schultz, J.S. Chem. Engng. Sci. 1974, 29, 12-23.
11. Kimura, S.G.; Walmet, G.F. Sep. Sci. Technol. 1980, 15, 1115-1133.
12. Bhave, R.R.; Sirkar, K.K. J. Membrane Sci. 1986, 27, 41-61.
13. Bhave, R.R.; Sirkar, K.K. manuscript submitted for publication, 1986.
14. Matson, S.L.; Herrick, C.S.; Ward, W.J. Ind. Eng. Chem. Proc. Des. Dev. 1977, 16, 370-374.
15. Ward, W.J. AIChE J. 1970, 16, 405.
16. Ward, W.J. Nature (London) 1970, 227, 162.
17. Otto, N.C.; Quinn, J.A. Chem. Engng. Sci. 1971, 26, 949-961.
18. Donaldson, T.L.; Quinn, J.A. Chem. Engng. Sci. 1975, 39, 103-115.
19. Bateman, B.R.; Way, J.D.; Larson, K.M. Sep. Sci. Technol. 1984 19, 21-32.
20. Bhave, R.R.; Sirkar, K.K. Final Contract Report, Celgard Business Unit 1983.
21. Deetz, D.W.; Zook, J.D. Eighth ACS Rocky Mountain Regional Meeting Abstracts 1986, Paper No. 251.
22. LeBlanc, O.H.; Ward, W.J.; Matson, S.L.; Kimura, S.G. J. Membrane Sci. 1980, 6, 339-343.
23. Pye, D.G.; Hoehn, H.H.; Panar, M. J. Appl. Polym. Sci. 1976, 20, 287-301.

RECEIVED January 9, 1987

Chapter 11

Stabilized Ultrathin Liquid Membranes for Gas Separations

David W. Deetz[1]

Honeywell, Inc., Physical Sciences Center, Bloomington, MN 55420

Although immobilized liquid membranes have the desirable properties of high selectivity and permeability, their practical application to gas phase separations is hindered because of the instability of the liquid phase and the relative thickness of current membranes. The problem of liquid instability, which is due to both liquid volatilization and flooding, can be reduced, or eliminated, by immobilizing the liquid phase in pores small enough to significantly reduce the molar free energy of the solution via the Kelvin effect. The obstacle of membrane thickness can be overcome by selectively immobilizing the liquid phase into the skin of a porous asymmetric membranes.

Membrane systems for the separation of gases are attractive because of both the low capital and operation costs, along with the low energy requirements. Unfortunately, the high performance selective membranes required for most applications do not yet exist. The major obstacle to be overcome is the development of membranes which simultaneously have the high selectivities and fluxes required for energy efficient operation.

Solid polymer membranes for gas separations have been widely investigated for many years. In order to maximize fluxes, asymmetric versions of polymer membranes with a very thin (~ 1 μ) membrane "skin" have been developed (1,2). Unfortunately these ultra-thin polymer membranes are still short of the flux needed for many applications. Also, the selectivity of the membranes to gases is often poor and thus, limits their usefulness.

Another approach to achieving high fluxes, besides making the membrane thinner, is to use a material which has a higher permeability. Liquids are inherently much more permeable than solid polymers. This is due to both the high gas diffusion coefficients in liquids (approximately 1000 times greater than in solid polymers) and the high gas/vapor solubilities in liquids. Immobilized liquid membranes (ILMs), which are composed of liquids immobilized in a porous polymer matrix (3), not only have high permeabilities, but are also simultaneously highly selective unlike polymer membranes.

Although immobilized liquid membranes are much more permeable and selective than solid polymer membranes, they have two deficiencies which need to be remedied before they can be effectively utilized. Firstly, they are not stable over long periods of time. The short lifetime of the membranes is mainly due to the loss of the liquid phase by evaporation. Current liquid membranes can only be used if the gas stream flowing past the membrane is first saturated with the liquid used in the membrane, or, if the membrane liquid is replaced frequently.

[1]Current address: PPG Industries, Inc., One PPG Place, Pittsburgh, PA 15272

The second problem with immobilized liquid membranes is that they are relatively thick (25-150 μ) compared to ultra-thin supported polymer membranes (0.1-2 μ). Since flux is inversely proportional to membrane thickness, this reduces the total flux achievable. Although methods of fabricating supported ultra-thin polymer membranes has been known for some time, there has been no method of preparing similar ultra-thin liquid membranes.

In the following two sections approaches for overcoming the limitations of immobilized liquid membranes are discussed. In the first section a method of reducing the evaporation of the liquid phase via the Kelvin effect is investigated. The second section reports on methods to fabricate supported ultra-thin liquid membranes.

Liquid Membrane Stabilization

Problems with ILM Stability.   Immobilized liquid membranes (ILM), pioneered by Ward, consist of microporous polymeric membrane impregnated by liquid which is selectively permeable to the desired gas (4).   ILMs offer some very important advantages over conventional solid membranes. One of their most important features are their simultaneous high permeability and selectivity. This characteristic has not been realized with either solid or porous polymer membranes. Another important feature of ILMs is the short development time required to tailor-make a selective membrane for a specific application.

Although ILMs offer some distinct performance advantages, they have some deficiencies which severely limit their usefulness.   The major obstacle to the widespread application of ILMs is their lack of stability. Because of the volatility of the liquid phases, most ILM have a short useful lifetime due to evaporation. Although the evaporation problem can be eliminated by saturating the feed gas with same liquid as is found in the membrane, this pretreatment is not practical for most applications.   In order to overcome the stability limitations of ILMs, a method to reduce the vapor pressure of the liquid phase is needed.

Utilization of the Kelvin Effect for ILM Stability.   One possible method for reducing the vapor pressure of immobilized liquids involves the expanded use of the capillary forces responsible for immobilization.   The reduction of the size of the pores in which the liquid is immobilized can have a significant effect on the liquid vapor pressure, and ultimately on ILM stability.   This vapor-pressure/pore-size relationship was derived by Lord Kelvin and is known as the Kelvin effect.

Explanation of the Kelvin effect. The vapor pressure of a liquid can be reduced if it is confined to a series of small capillary-like pores with diameters of 0.2 microns or less . The relationship between the magnitude of the vapor pressure reduction and pore radius is given by the Kelvin equation

$$P/P_o = e^{-2\gamma M/\rho R T r'} \tag{1}$$

where P/P_o is the ratio of the vapor pressure of the liquid in the pore relative to the vapor pressure of the bulk liquid, γ is the surface tension, M is the molecular weight, ρ is the liquid density, R is the gas constant, T is the absolute temperature and r′ is the effective radius of the pores as defined in Figure 1.

Figure 2 demonstrates the reduction of vapor pressure as calculated from the Kelvin equation for various liquids in small pores.   The Kelvin effect for capillaries was verified in 1979 and has been experimentally measured down to 40 angstroms (5).

For the common case in which a liquid is exposed to an inert gas such as air and in which the vapor pressure of the liquid is much less than the absolute pressure of the gas the Kelvin effect can be explained as follows (6). The reduction in the vapor pressure of the liquid is due to the liquid's decreased absolute pressure **P** in the pores. This

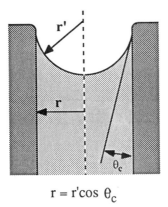

$$r = r'\cos\,\theta_c$$

Figure 1. Diagram of Liquid in a Uniform Pore

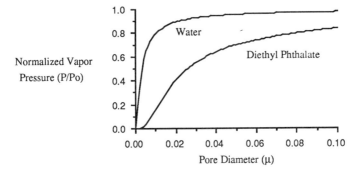

Figure 2. The Vapor Pressure of an Immobilized Liquid as a Function of
Pore Size

reduction is the result of the concave surface which is formed at the gas-liquid interface.
If a liquid wets the walls of the pore, the liquid surface is thereby constrained to lie
parallel (or close to parallel if the contact angle is non-zero) to the wall, and the
complete surface must therefore be concave in shape (Figure 1). Because the interface
is curved, the surface tension causes the absolute pressure on the liquid side to be
reduced. The pressure difference ΔP across this interface is given by the Young and
Laplace equation, which for a hemispherical surface is:

$$\Delta P = 2\gamma\,/\,r' \qquad\qquad\qquad (2)$$

where ΔP is the decrease in the absolute pressure. The reduction in absolute pressure
decreases the molar free energy G of the liquid and thereby reduces the vapor pressure.
The molar free energy can be related to absolute pressure by

$$\Delta G = \int V \, d \, \mathbf{P} \tag{3}$$

where V is the molar volume, which in this case is considered to be constant. The vapor pressure of a liquid is a function of the molar free energy and it can be seen from the equation

$$G = G° + RT \ln P \tag{4}$$

that when G decreases the vapor pressure is also reduced.

Although Lord Kelvin developed the equation describing the relationship between the vapor pressure of liquids immobilized in pores and pore diameter in the late nineteen hundreds, it was not verified until 1979 (5). Fisher verified the Kelvin equation only for pure liquids.   It is not clear what effect small capillaries would have on the vapor pressure of solutions, although, some literature (7) suggests that the vapor pressure suppression effect should be synergistically enhanced with the presence of solutes.

In the following sections an example of the applicability of the Kelvin effect will be presented.   The effect of pore size on the stability of aqueous membranes will be investigated.

Special Stability Problems with Aqueous Membranes. Aqueous-based ILMs are one of the most important and most studied types of ILMs. Aqueous solution membranes with high concentrations of electrolytes are very useful because they are one of the best barriers to nitrogen and oxygen.   This is important for separations in ambient conditions when it is desirable to remove or collect trace gases or vapors while not collecting either oxygen or nitrogen. Also, aqueous membranes support many highly-selective carrier molecules. The problem with aqueous ILMs is that they are especially susceptible to stability problems. The stability problems of aqueous ILMs is due to 1) the high vapor pressure of water, and, 2) the varying background partial pressures of water vapor present in ambient atmospheres. The high vapor pressure of water in the ILM results in rapid evaporation of the aqueous membrane during exposure to dry environments. When the relative humidity is high, an aqueous membrane with a high ionic strength will often "flood", i.e., the salt solution in the membrane will absorb water until it overfills the porous support and runs down the membrane surface. Because of the conflicting problems of evaporation and flooding, aqueous membranes are stable only over a small humidity range. An aqueous/Cs_2CO_2 ILM developed for CO_2 separation by Ward required an environment containing 70-85% R.H. for effective use (8).

In order to make aqueous ILMs practical, a method of eliminating the evaporation problem is needed. This can be done by reducing the vapor pressure of water in the membrane below the lowest partial pressure of water vapor in the feed gas. In ambient environments in which the relative humidity ranges from 10-90%, this means the vapor pressure of the water in the membrane should be less than 2 mm•Hg. A method of reducing the vapor pressure of the immobilized liquid is needed which does not increase the flooding problem.

Although increasing the concentration of solutes reduces the vapor pressures of aqueous solutions, it does not increase the usable humidity range since it magnifies the flooding problem. An aqueous solution which is saturated will also have only a narrow range of humidities, approximately 10-20%, in which it is stable. The mean value of the range is determined by the solute concentration.

In the following section, the Kelvin effect on aqueous solutions is investigated for the purpose of developing a stable water-based liquid membrane.

Investigation of Kelvin Effect on Aqueous Solutions.
Methods. In order to determine the relationship between pore size and vapor pressure the solutions were immobilized in porous structures and a method was devised to measure the resulting vapor pressure. These areas are discussed below.

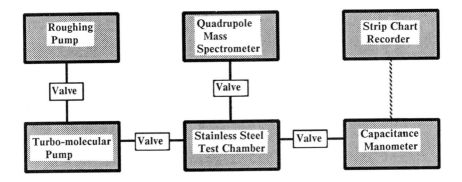

Figure 3. Schematic Diagram of Vapor Pressure Test Apparatus

A. Liquid Immobilization. Polymeric membranes made of cellulose nitrate (Millipore MF-series) were used to immobilize the solutions. These membranes do not have the well defined pore configuration and size distribution of track-etched membranes but rather have a sponge-like pore structure and a known average pore size. These membranes were used for the tests because the polycarbonate track-etched membranes (Nuclepore PC-series) were not chemically compatible with the lithium bromide used in the solutions. Another reason for using cellulose nitrate as porous material is that the contact angle between it and water is very small, approximately 18 degrees, and thus the liquid wets the membrane quickly and the effective pore size is only 5% larger than the membrane pore size.

B. Apparatus Design. A literature review on vapor pressure measurement uncovered no "standard" test system which might be used for this application. Figure 3 shows the system designed and used for measuring vapor pressure.

The specific hardware used in the vapor pressure test equipment included a MKS 390 absolute-pressure capacitance manometer (100 torr full scale) for pressure measurement, a Keithly thermocouple system for temperature measurement, a MKS 398 differential capacitance manometer (1 torr full scale) with molecular flow element for mass flow measurement, an Alcatel model 86 turbomolecular pump with an Alcatel roughing pump as backing for pumping, and a dual pen Honeywell strip chart recorder for data storage. The vacuum system components were made of stainless steel and VCR vacuum fittings with copper gaskets were used for connections.

C. Test Procedure. The test procedure for vapor pressure determination was as follows:

1.) Place sample in test chamber (The test chamber consisted of a 4 inch viewport with an o-ring seal. A flange with a tube with a VCR fitting served as the top to the chamber. The total volume of the chamber was very small: approximately 10 cc.).

2.) Evacuate the chamber with vacuum pumps for 5 seconds (This will not only eliminate most of the ambient air but will also remove the liquid vapor present, temporarily upsetting the gas-liquid equilibrium.).

3.) Close valve to pumps and allow the absolute pressure in the test chamber to equilibrate (After the test chamber is closed off the total pressure in the test chamber increases because of the liquid molecules going into the gas phase to re-establish equilibrium.).

4.) Measure resulting absolute pressure with capacitance manometer (The measurement is recorded after the pressure has stabilized. Also the system temperature is recorded at this time since vapor pressure is a function of temperature.).

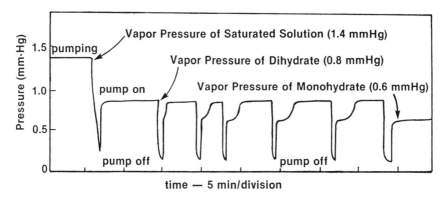

Figure 4. Determination of the multiple vapor pressures found in saturated LiBr solutions

Results. Control experiments were done to confirm the accuracy of the vapor measurement technique used. Bulk solutions were placed in small glass containers and the vapor pressure measured. The vapor pressure of distilled water was determined to be 23.0 mmHg at 24±1 degrees C., which agrees well with the value of 22.3 mmHg at 24 degrees obtained from the Chemical Rubber Company Handbook of Chemistry and Physics. The vapor pressure of a saturated NaBr solution was measured to be 12.4 mmHg at 22±1 degrees C., in good agreement with the reported value of 13.4 mmHg at 25 degrees C. (9).

Next, controls were done to characterize the LiBr solution in bulk form. The vapor pressure of saturated LiBr solution was measured and found to be 1.4 mmHg at 21±1 degrees Celcius. This value is consistent with previous experimental results of 1.8 mmHg at 25 degrees C. (10).

The sample was then successively pumped on to remove water, and two more pressure plateaus became evident (Figure 4). These plateaus were interpreted as the vapor pressures of the di- and mono- hydrated LiBr crystals. At the transition between the original and second plateaus, the solution changed from being transparent to translucent. This would be consistent with a change from the clear saturated solution to the white crystalline dihydrate. Also, a one-to-one relationship between the number of moles of water that could be removed after the onset of the third plateau, and the number of moles of LiBr present in the system, was measured with a molecular flow element. No further plateaus were found down to 0.01 mmHg. These observations suggest that the second and third plateaus in Figure 5 represent the vapor pressures of the di- and mono- hydrated LiBr crystals.

The water vapor pressures of the dihydrate and monohydrate LiBr crystals were determined to be 0.85 mmHg and 0.6 mmHg at 21 degrees C. respectively (Figure 5). From discussions with D. Boryta (Foote Mineral Company), an author of several papers on LiBr characteristics, and from the results of literature searches it appears that these measurements are the first direct measurements of the equilibrium vapor pressures taken.

The vapor pressure of pure water in a porous membrane (0.22μ pore diameter) was measured and found to the same as bulk water. This is consistent with the Kelvin equation, which predicts only an one percent reduction in vapor pressure. Next, the vapor pressures of saturated LiBr solutions in porous membranes of various pore diameters were measured. The results obtained from these measurements are shown in Figure 5.

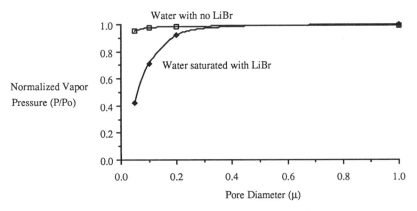

Figure 5. Effect of Pore Size on an Aqueous Solution with High Ionic Strength

Along with vapor pressure, condensation rate is also an important parameter in membrane stability. The condensation rate is a measure of the liquid membrane's ability to replenish its liquid content and is especially important when the membrane is used with backside pumping. Condensation rates were measured as a function of pore size for the aqueous LiBr liquid membrane. Figure 6 illustrates the dependence of condensation rate on pore size. These results, along with the vapor pressure results, indicate that polymer supports with small pore diameters should be used to optimize aqueous membrane stability.

Discussion. The results from the experiments on vapor pressure show that the vapor pressure of an aqueous solution can be reduced when it is immobilized in small sponge-like pores. The extent of the vapor pressure reduction is approximately one order of magnitude greater than predicted by the Kelvin equation, which was derived and verified using uniform capillaries, when the following values were used in the calculations: $\gamma = 71$ dyne/cm, $\rho = 1.0$ gm/ml, $M = 18$ g/mole, contact angle = 18 degrees, and r was the nominal pore radius given by the manufacturer. For example, the Kelvin equation would predict a 7% decrease in vapor pressure for the aqueous lithium bromide solution in a 0.025μ diameter pore, yet a 54% decrease was observed. Similarly, a 2% decrease in vapor pressure for the 0.1μ pore diameter is predicted while a 29% reduction was measured. These initial results would seem to indicate one of three things:

1. The Kelvin equation, which describes the relationship between the vapor pressure of pure liquids in small pores and pore diameter, does not accurately predict the relationship in the more complicated case of liquids with dissolved solutes.
2. The sponge-like pores used for the tests may not be a suitable analog for the uniform capillaries used to derive and verify the Kelvin equation.

<u>Development of a Stable Aqueous Membrane.</u> An aqueous LiBr membrane was fabricated by soaking a porous 47 mm diameter cellulose acetate/nitrate membrane in a 3 M LiBr solution for 24 hours. The membrane was then exposed to a vacuum for 5 hours to remove the water while leaving the lithium bromide. It was then placed into the apparatus shown in Figure 7 and exposed to a nitrogen mixture containing approximately 10 mmHg water vapor until the pores filled via condensation.

Stability Testing. The boundaries of the humidity range in which an aqueous membrane is stable are determined on the low end by liquid phase evaporation and at

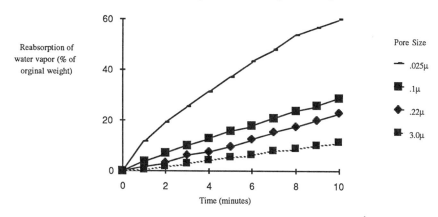

Figure 6. Reabsorption of water for membranes with different pore diameters.

the high end by liquid flooding. The evaporation of the liquid phase can determined by 1) a visual change in the membrane from translucent to opaque and 2) a radical change in total membrane flux and selectivity. The aqueous LiBr membrane was exposed a nitrogen stream mixed with varying amounts of water vapor. The membrane evaporation point was determined by the above methods to be 4 ± 1 % R. H. at 25 ° C.

The point at which flooding occurs can be measured optically by having a light source on the membrane and observing the reflectance change. The membrane, which normally is non-reflective due to the very irregular surface structure of the porous matrix, becomes very reflective at the onset of flooding. The onset of flooding, which is strongly a function of pore size, was measured at 90% R. H. for an aqueous/LiBr membrane utilizing a cellulose acetate/nitrate matrix with 0.05 μ pore diameters.

When the aqueous/LiBr membrane is exposed to a gas with less than the equivalent of 3% R. H. humidity the aqueous phase evaporates. It is interesting to note that upon re-exposure to higher humidities, water vapor condenses and refills the pores to the original levels. This property of self-regeneration is demonstrated in Figure 8. The membrane was placed in the apparatus shown in Figure 7 and the pressure on the vacuum side was measured. The measured pressure is a function of the total flux through membrane. During exposure to dry nitrogen (Fig. 8) the aqueous phase of the membrane evaporated, allowing the free convection of nitrogen through the porous matrix. Upon exposure to a more humid mixture, water vapor condensated in the pores and refilled the membrane, thus, resulting in a decreased measured pressure.

Discussion. The method and technique used for fabrication of the aqueous liquid membranes are very important in achieving good stability. Membranes filled by condensation methods are much more stable than those which are soaked and allowed to dry. One possible reason for this may be that the condensation method avoids the problem of overfilling and thus ensures good curvature at the pore openings.

It is also important when using hygroscopic liquids to underfill the membranes to allow for changes in liquid volume. Although the use of matrices with small pores reduces the uptake of water with changes in humidity, an excess of capacity in the matrix can further extend the usable humidity range. This concept of a variable-volume liquid membrane is useful when using hygroscopic liquids such polyethylene glycol and high ionic strength aqueous solutions.

The choice of the polymer support for the liquid membrane matrix is function of not only pore size but also of chemical compatibility (11). For a ILM with a long lifetime, a matrix material which is inert to the liquid phase is required. The cellulose acetate/nitrate supports used in these experiments, which lost their initial structural

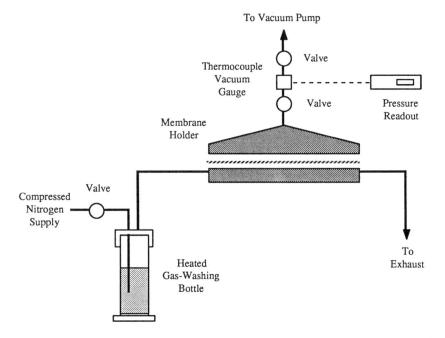

Figure 7. Apparatus for Ultra-thin Membrane Fabrication

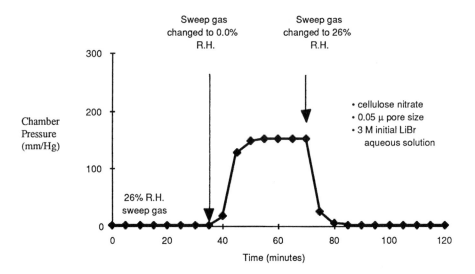

Figure 8. Experimental Results Demonstrating the Self-regeneration properties of the Aqueous/LiBr Liquid Membrane

strength over time, are not recommended for this application. Polysulfone porous supports have much greater resistance to aqueous electrolytes.

Another problem associated with support selection is lack of homogeneity of pore size. Many of the membrane supports initially used have larger pores in the mid-section of the support than on the surface due to the casting methods used. If only the large pores of the middle are filled, a vapor pressure reduction much less than predicted is observed. It is important to select a support with uniform pore size to avoid unexpected problems.

Although only aqueous membranes with LiBr were discussed in the preceding sections, the concept of stabilizing liquid membranes via the Kelvin effect applies to other liquid systems as well. Similar results have been observed using other electrolytes in an aqueous system. Non-aqueous liquids, especially those with molecular weights above 100 with high surface tensions, can also be stabilized in a similar fashion.

Ultra-Thin Liquid Membranes

Objective. The flux across a membrane determines the amount of membrane surface area needed for a given application. The higher the flux, the lower the amount of surface area of membrane required. Since flux is inversely proportional to membrane thickness, and since membrane area is the dominating factor in system capital costs, the importance of reducing membrane thickness is evident.

The thickness of ILMs is determined by the thickness of the porous matrix used. Common matrices are symmetrical porous polymers with thicknesses of 25 to 150 μ. The selection of the matrix thickness is a trade off between desired flux and structural strength. A thin matrix results in an ILM with high flux and little structural strength, while a thick matrix results in an ILM with low flux and good structural strength. For many industrial applications even the thinnest conventional ILMs (25μ) have too low a flux for efficient operation. Thinner ILMs with sufficient structural strength are needed. The objective of the study discussed in this section is to investigate methods of fabricating supported ultra-thin ILM.

Approach One approach to the development of a very thin membrane with good mechanical strength is to integrate a structure with distinct selective and supporting elements. An example of this would be a thin selective layer supported by a thick porous layer. Since the functionality of the two elements are now separated, the flux and mechanical strength can be manipulated independently to meet the application requirements.

This has been done previously with solid polymer membranes. Loeb and Sourirajan (2) developed polymer dope recipes and casting/coagulation procedures which made possible the formation of asymmetric membranes comprised of a very thin (0.1-1.0 μm) "skin" layer resting atop a much thicker(~100μm) microporous substrate region. For gas phase operation, the film is annealed to produce a dense pore-free skin. Another type of ultra-thin polymer membrane, the supported ultra-thin membrane (1), involves the creation of a two layer laminate in which the thin and selective film is supported by a microporous backing. The backing is made sufficiently porous so as to minimize its flow resistance, while its pores are made sufficiently small that the burst strength of the thin membrane is not exceeded where it spans the mouth of a pore.

ILMs can be fabricated with any any porous matrix in which the liquid phase wets the matrix material and the pores are sufficiently small. Since commercially available asymmetric membranes with thin (0.1 - 2μm) porous skins supported by a macroporous backing exist, it should be possible to fabricate liquid membrane versions of the supported ultra-thin polymer membranes (Figure 9).

Methods of Preparation. The major obstacle to fabricating ultra-thin membranes with asymmetric supports is finding a method to selectively immobilize the liquid phase in

Thin (0.1-1.5μ) liquid layer immobilized
in a porous polymer skin

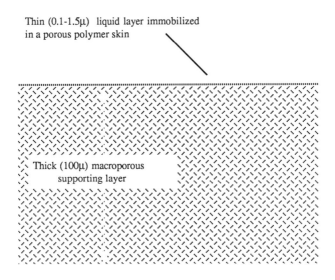

**Figure 9. Cross-section representation of an ultra-thin (asymmetric) liquid
membrane**

the microporous skin while leaving the macroporous support free of liquid. If the
support area is also wetted the membrane will behave essentially as a conventional
ILM.

Three methods have been developed for selectively immobilizing the liquid phase in
the skin rather than the support of the asymmetric membranes. The methods are:

1.) *Selective condensation of liquid phase into skin.* The liquid phase can be applied
to the skin layer of the porous membrane by exposing to a gas saturated with the
desired liquid vapor. If the pores are small enough, the liquid will condense and fill
the small pores in the skin. Condensation occurs selectively because of the reduced
chemical potential of liquids in small pores. The process can be monitored and
controlled by assembling the simple apparatus in Figure 7. The membrane is placed
in a membrane holder with the skin layer exposed to the feed gas and the support
exposed to the vacuum Initially the skin is exposed to dry nitrogen in order to
remove any adsorbed vapors and the valves to the vaccuum pump are opened.
After a baseline pressure is achieved, the skin is *slowly* exposed to nitrogen
saturated with the desired liquid vapor. In some cases it is advantageous to heat the
gas in order to increase the vapor concentration, although too much heating results
in bulk condensation on the membrane surface. When all of the pores in the surface
layer are filled with liquid the pressure of on the vaccuum side will sharply decrease
and stabilize. The magnitude of the pressure decrease depends on the porosity of
the skin, the composition of the liquid phase and the carrier gas used. This method
works well with homogeneous liquids, but is not suitable with heterogeneous
solutions.

2.) *Direct application of liquid to skin.* Another method of establishing the liquid phase is to apply the liquid directly to the skin. This can be done in two ways. The first is to carefully use a paint brush, or other device, to apply a limited amount of liquid to the surface of the skin layer. The progress can be monitored by utilizing a system similar to the one in Figure 7 fitted with a membrane holder with an open feed side. The pressure drop again can be used as an indicator of liquid coverage. The disadvantage of this method is poor control over membrane thickness and also variability of the membranes. The second method is to float the ultra-thin porous membrane, skin side down, on the surface of the desired liquid for a given period of time. This method works well with heterogeneous solutions such as water with dissolved solids, but it use is limited to liquids with a high surface tension. The surface tension keeps the membrane afloat so that only the skin pores are exposed to the liquid.

3.) *Bulk application of liquid and selective removal from support.* The third method is unlike the other two, in that, the entire matrix (skin and support) are immersed in the desired liquid, and the liquid in the supporting matrix is selectively removed. After the matrix is soaked in solution, the support side is exposed to a vacuum The liquid in the supporting matrix is selectively removed due to the higher vapor pressure, and therefore evaporation rate, of the liquid in the large pores of the support relative to the small pores of the support.

The optimum method to be used is determined by the nature of the liquid phase to be immobilized. In some cases it is desirable to a combination of the techniques.

<u>An Example of an Ultra-Thin Liquid Membrane.</u> An ultra-thin version of the aqueous/LiBr membrane was developed. The membrane was fabricated by floating a 47 mm diameter asymmetric cellulose acetate membrane (Amicon) on a 6.9 M LiBr solution for 24 hours. The membrane was then exposed to a vacuum for 5 hours to remove the water while leaving the lithium bromide. It was then exposed to a nitrogen/oxygen mixture containing approximately 10 mmHg water vapor until the pores filled.

During fabrication it is important to monitor the status of the membrane and verify the existance of the thin liquid layer. This can be done by measuring the flux through the membrane and the membrane selectivity. Both parameters change sharply when the skin pores fill. The existence of the liquid layer in the ultra-thin aqueous/LiBr membrane was verified by a 3 fold drop in pressure on the vacuum side and a change in the oxygen/nitrogen ratio measured with an attached quadrapole mass spectrometer. The membrane matrix was weighed before and after the treatment in order to determine a mean membrane thickness. The weight gain of the membrane was 3 mg which would translate into an average aqueous layer thickness of 2 microns.

The membrane remained stable over 35 days of testing in which a vaccuum was pulled on the support side while the skin side was exposed to ambient conditions. Both the pressure drop and the oxygen/nitrogen ratio were measured over this period.

The membrane also exhibited the same self-repair properties as the thicker (100 μ) aqueous LiBr membrane (see Figure 8). After having the water removed from the matrix by extended exposure to dry nitrogen (> 0.01% R.H.), the liquid phase was regenerated upon exposure to ambient conditions.

<u>Conclusion</u>

The objective of this study was to investigate methods of overcoming the limitations of ILMs so that their virtues of high selectivity and flux could be utilized. The conclusions are as follows.

1. *The stability of ILMs can be significantly improved.* The evaporation of the liquid phase, the limiting factor in ILM lifetime, can be reduced by decreasing the liquid's radius of curvature at the gas/liquid interface. This is accomplished by selecting a support with very small pore diameters. In order to maximize the effect of the small pores, it is advantageous to apply the liquid in vapor form and allow the pores to fill by condensation. When hygroscopic liquids are used, the selection of pore size is again important to minimize flooding problems. Designing the membrane for variable volume operation also helps to reduce this problem.

2. *Ultra-thin liquid membranes can be fabricated down to 1 μ in thickness.* Ultra-thin liquid membranes can be formed in the skin layer of an porous asymmetric polymer membrane by methods in which the liquid is selectively deposited in the skin rather than the backing support. The wide variety of pore sizes and membrane configurations available in asymmetric membranes allows for good flexibility in the design of ultra-thin liquid membrane systems.

The inherent properties of liquids allows for the development of membranes capable of efficient one-step separations not possible previously with solid polymer membranes. The advantages of utilizing liquids as the membrane substrate rather than solids are as follows:

a) *High Selectivity.* The large differences in the gas/vapor solubilities of various liquid phases allow for the development of highly selective membranes. It is possible to fabricate stable ILMs composed of homogeneous liquids with selectivity ratios greater than a 100,000 to 1. To further enhance performance, facilitator molecules can be added to many liquid membranes. In the case of the ultra-thin liquid membranes, the choices of facilitators is limited to those with very rapid reaction times since the diffusion time across the membrane is very short.

b) *High Flux.* Because of their high gas diffusion coefficients (1000x greater than in solids) and the solubilities, liquid membranes are inherently permeable. Homogeneous liquid membranes with permeabilities approaching those of microporous membranes (100,000 Barrer) are possible. The fabrication of ILMs in ultra-thin form enhances the already high flux, such that, in some cases the boundary layer of gas passing over the membrane acts as a greater barrier than the membrane itself. In this case the design of a system in which the boundary layer thickness is minimized becomes the paramount concern.

c) *No Pin Hole Problems.* When solids are cast very thin, pin hole problems frequently occur. The occurrence of pin holes results in the convective transfer of gases across the membrane and thus a reduction in selectivity. Pin hole densities as low as 10^{-6} % are enough to prevent a membrane from effectively separating gases (12). Because of the nature of liquids, this is not a problem in ILMs.

d) *Short Development Time.* Due to the extensive data base available on liquid systems, the performance of a ILM system can be predicted or easily determined. No new materials need to be developed. Because of these factors the time required to develop a new highly selective membrane can be short.

Acknowledgment

I would like to express my gratitude to C. Anderson, N. Newkumet, and G. Drier for their experimental contributions. I would also like to acknowledge the significant contributions made by Prof. M. Kreevoy of the University of Minnesota, who acted as a catalyst for much of this work.

Literature Cited

1. Riley, R. L. ; Lonsdale, H. K. ; Lyons, C. R. ; Merten, U. ; J. Appl. Polymer Science 1967, 11, 2143.
2. Loeb, S. ; Sourirajan, S. ; Saline Water Conversion II, p. 117. Advances in Chemistry Series No. 38. American Chemical Society 1962.
3. Ward, W. J. ; Robb, W. L. Science 1967, 156, 1481.
4. Way, J. D. ; Noble, R. D. ; Flynn, T. M. ; Sloan, E. D. J. Membr. Sci. 1982, 12, 239.
5. Fisher, L. R. ; Isrealachvili, J. N. Nature, 1979, 277, 548.
6. Adamson, A. W., Physical Chemistry of Surfaces, Wiley-Interscience, New York, 1982.
7. Folman, M. ; Shereshefsky, J. L. Jour. of Phys. Chem., 1955, 59, 607.
8. Ward, W. J. ; Report No. AMRL-TR-67-53, Aerospace Medical Research Laboratories, Wright-Patterson Air Force Base, 1967.
9. Pearce, J. N., Taylor, M. ; Bartlett, R. M. J. of Phy. Chemistry,1928, 50, 2951.
10. Boryta, D. A. ; Maas, A. J. ; Grant, C. B. J. of Chem. and Eng. Data, 1975, 20, No. 3.
11. Way, J. D. ; Noble, R. D. ; Bateman, B. R. In Materials Science of Synthetic Membranes; Lloyd, D. R., Ed.; ACS Symposium Series No. 269; American Chemical Society: Washington D.C., 1985; pp 119-128.
12. Henis, M. S. ; Tripodi, M. K. Science, 1983, 220, No. 4592, 11.

RECEIVED January 9, 1987

Chapter 12

Extractive Ultrafiltration
A Two-Stage Waste-Water Cleanup Process Based on Extraction and Ultrafiltration

James C. Watters[1], David G. Murrer[1,3], Marvin Fleischman[1], and Elias Klein[2]

[1]Chemical Engineering Department, University of Louisville, Louisville, KY 40292
[2]Division of Nephrology, School of Medicine, University of Louisville, Louisville, KY 40292

Extractive ultrafiltration combines the separation operations of extraction and ultrafiltration to remove trace levels of organic contaminants from industrial wastewaters. The wastewater is contacted with an emulsion phase, the organic part of which is insoluble in water but selectively extracts contaminants present in the water. The emulsion is then separated using an ultrafilter. The permeate is clean water; the retentate, containing the emulsion oil, the contaminant and the surfactant, is recycled.

The feasibility of operating this process continuously has been demonstrated using toluene as the contaminant and heptane as the extracting solvent. Initial concentrations of toluene of 400-450 ppm were consistently reduced to less than 10% of those values in the permeate during approximately five hours of running time. The process is expected to be of use to industries which generate small to medium quantities of wastewater containing trace amounts of organic contaminants which might otherwise be difficult and/or expensive to remove.

The chemical, petrochemical, textile, and metal finishing industries typically produce many different types of wastewaters which contain various concentrations of toxic organic and inorganic substances. In

[3]Current address: Frito-Lay, Inc., Charlotte, NC 28217

0097-6156/87/0347-0166$06.00/0

most cases these pollutants are still present in trace quantities
even after being treated by conventional means such as biological
oxidation or alum coagulation. Further treatment is usually required
to remove these contaminants before the streams are discharged into
the environment.

In the settlement of a law suit brought against the Environmental Protection Agency, EPA, by several environmental groups, the
EPA agreed in 1976 to review the effluent limitations and guidelines
of 65 toxic chemicals based on the best available technology economically achievable (1-2). As a result of the Clean Water Act, CWA, in
1977, the EPA expanded this list to 129. This is commonly known as
the Priority Pollutant List. The Clean Water Act requires that
effluent standards be established for each toxic pollutant.

Many different technologies have been applied for treating waste
water streams. Steam stripping (1), packed tower aeration, PTA,
(3), and granular activated carbon, GAC, (3) adsorption are just a
few of the techniques that have been successful in selectively
removing trace organic pollutants from aqueous streams. However,
these methods of contaminant removal are quite expensive and usually
lend themselves to the treatment of large quantities of wastewater.
It is desired to develop a technology that will economically remove
pollutants from small volumes of wastewater streams.

The present paper proposes a technology for removing trace
organic pollutants from wastewater using extraction in series with
ultrafiltration. Extraction is viewed as an attractive removal
method because certain organic contaminants are more soluble in
organic oils than in water. Barbarl et. al. (4), found large distribution coefficients for 17 compounds on the EPA priority pollutant
list using undecane as an extraction solvent. The large surface area
of an oil/water emulsion provides a favorable extraction environment
for the contaminant to diffuse from the aqueous phase to the organic
phase. The two phases can be separated easily using ultrafiltration,
a technique which is well documented in the literature (5-15).

The objective of the current research was to test the concept of
continuous extractive-ultrafiltration using toluene as a single
organic contaminant. Toluene, which is on the EPA priority pollutant
list, was extracted into a heptane/water emulsion. A surfactant
was used to form a stable emulsion with a large area for mass transfer and to minimize the passage of heptane through the ultrafiltration membrane. The emulsion was processed through a Romicon hollow
fiber ultrafiltration membrane. It was expected that the water
passing through the ultrafiltration membrane would contain a
decreased toluene concentration compared to the toluene concentration
in the feed.

An experimental apparatus for continuously processing an aqueous
stream containing an organic contaminant was designed and
constructed. The criteria for choosing the contaminant/surfactant/
extraction solvent are discussed along with the system operating
parameters such as the heptane/water ratio, the hydrodynamic
conditions of the ultrafilter and the overall efficiency of the
toluene separation. A mathematical model of the continuous system
was also developed and evaluated.

Characteristics of the Experimental System

The experimental system used to continuously process a wastewater stream by extraction followed by ultrafiltration is shown in Figure 1. A wastewater stream containing a single organic contaminant was pumped from the feed tank to the process tank. Here, the contaminant was extracted into an organic oil that had been emulsified with a surfactant. The oil/water emulsion was then pumped through an ultrafilter where the oil was returned to the process tank. The permeate passing through the membrane contained a lower concentration of organic contaminant than was in the feed. Free oil, as well as fragments of the surfactant polymer, were also expected to pass through the membrane into the permeate. However, this passage was minimized by using a high concentration of a high molecular weight surfactant.

   In specifying the contaminant/surfactant/extraction solvent system to be studied, it was desirable for the system to have the following characteristics:

1. The oil should be less soluble in water than the contaminant.
2. The analysis of the contaminant/extraction oil system should be an accurate and straightforward process.
3. The organic contaminant should be on the EPA priority pollutant list.
4. The nonionic polymeric surfactant must form a relatively stable emulsion.
5. The nonionic polymeric surfactant should be of a high molecular weight so that it does not pass through the membrane and consequently need to be accounted for in product stream analysis.
6. For the safety of the investigators the chemical system should be relatively easy and safe to handle.

   An extraction solvent/surfactant/contaminant system was found with these characteristics. The extraction oil or solvent used was heptane. Heptane is relatively insoluble in water, when compared with the contaminant, toluene. At $25°C$ heptane and toluene are soluble in water 2.83 ppm and 515 ppm respectively (16). Gas chromatography was used for analyzing the composition of the aqueous and organic phases. In an actual scaled-up version of this process another cheaper solvent, such as kerosene, might be substituted for heptane. Kerosene is a blend of so many compounds (76 were identified by us on a GC scan of one sample), including toluene, that it was not feasible to use it in our tests which required the identification of toluene in the retentate and feed streams. Once the feasibility of the process is proven we can switch to this cheaper solvent. Ultimate disposal of the kerosene, contaminated with the toluene could be by combustion of a bleed stream from the retentate or the process tank.

   The emulsifier was a blend of two nonionic-polymeric surfactants, poly(vinyl alchohol), PVA, and poly(ethylene oxide), PEO. Both polymers have molecular weights in excess of the membrane cutoff of 50,000 daltons. The average molecular weights of PVA and PEO are 125,000 and 100,000 respectively.

   The principle on which the separation is based is similar to that of emulsion liquid membranes wherein a contaminant is extracted

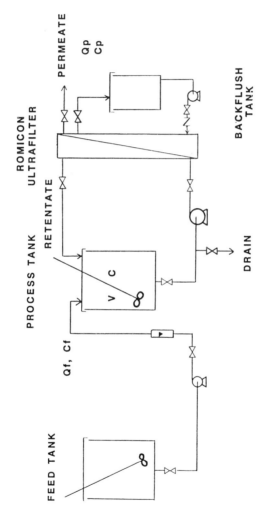

Figure 1. Schematic of the experimental system.

from an aqueous phase through an organic membrane into a phase in
which it is concentrated for ultimate disposal. In our case, however, we separate the extraction stage from the membrane part of the
process and use conventional ultrafiltration to separate our
emulsion.

Experimental Method

Apparatus. Both feed and process tanks in Figure 1 are 19-liter
polyethylene flat bottomed tanks which are covered to minimize
evaporation of toluene and heptane. The process tank was equipped
with a variable-speed twin-bladed agitator to dissolve the surfactant
and form the emulsion. The retentate, returned from the ultrafilter,
was somewhat elevated in temperature so that the fluid in the process
tank had to be cooled to room temperature by constantly pumping a
solution of water and ethylene glycol through an internal coil.
      The hollow fiber ultrafiltration unit used to separate the
heptane/water emulsion was a Romicon HFXS-MKII model. The system
contains a 1¼ inch by 1 inch, 3/4 HP centrifugal circulation pump,
a diaphragm pressure control valve and temperature and pressure
indicators. The Romicon HF1.1-45-XM50 Hollow Fiber membrane
cartridge has a nominal molecular weight cutoff of 50,000. The cartridge contains 50 parallel fibers potted at both ends of a 63.5 cm
(25.0 in) long by 2.54 cm (1.0 in) in diameter, plastic shell. The
inside diameter of these fibers is 1.1 mm (0.045 in). The process
stream flows through the inside of the fibers and the permeate
collects in the shell.

Materials. All organic solvents were manufactured by Fisher
Scientific Company. The extraction solvent heptane, and the trace
contaminant toluene, were of reagent and purified grades respectively. The internal standard for the gas chromatograph, methanol,
was certified ACS.
      Because of the impurities in the tap water, the water was
distilled using a Barnstead electric still and then filtered through
a Milli-Q Type I Reagent Grade Water Purifying System. The Milli-Q
System, manufactured by Cort Water Systems, was used to remove
dissolved organics in the distilled water.
      The two surfactant polymers used to stabilize the heptane and
water emulsion were poly(ethylene oxide), PEO, and poly(vinyl
alcohol), PVA. Poly(ethylene oxide), also known as Polyox, was
obtained from Union Carbide Corporation, South Charleston, West
Viriginia. Polyox WSR N-10, the grade of polymer used in this work,
had an average molecular weight of 100,000. The poly(vinyl alcohol)
used was marketed by Monsanto, St. Louis, Missouri, as Gelvatol
20/90. This polymer has an average molecular weight of 125,000.

Procedure

Much preliminary work was needed to determine quantities and compositions of emulsions to be used and the hydrodynamics of the membrane
system, and to develop an assay for toluene and heptane in the
various streams. This series of experiments is detailed by Murrer
(17). Based on his work, the emulsion compositions listed in Table
I were chosen for the continuous feasibility study. Inlet and outlet

pressures for the ultrafilter were set based on balancing permeate
flux, transmembrane pressure, hydraulic pressure gradient and fouling
of the membrane.

Table I. Pertinent Data for the Continuous Extraction
and Ultrafiltration of a Toluene/Water Solution

	Run 1	Run 2
Feed Tank Volume	18.9 ltr.	18.9 ltr.
Initial Toluene Conc.	455 ppm	420 ppm
Proc. Tk. Volume	5.0 ltr.	5.0 ltr.
% by vol. Heptane	10	30
% by vol. Water	90	70
Toluene Preload	25 ml	113 ml
Weight of PEO	25.0 gms	25.0 gms
Weight of PVA	25.0 gms	25.0 gms
Initial PHYD	$P_1=10.0$ @	$P_1=15.0$ @
of Ultrafilter (PSI)	$P_2=0.0$	$P_2=2.0$

P_1 = Inlet Pressure to the Ultrafilter
P_2 = Outlet (retentate) Pressure from the Ultrafilter

Gas chromatography, using a Varian Model 3700 GC, was chosen to
analyze the process streams. Methanol was a suitable internal
standard. The GC tuning parameters were set based on low toluene
concentration, so the permeate analyses are expected to be more
accurate than those of the feed or process tank contents. For this
reason 50 ppm of toluene was arbitrarily chosen as the maximum
allowable concentration in the permeate. In order to give run times
of about 5 hours duration the emulsion was preloaded with about 7%
toluene by volume so that the continuous runs modelled the end stages
of a commercial operation.

For the first run, 4.5 liters of distilled-millipore water were
measured into the process tank. Twenty-five grams of PEO and 25 gms.
of PVA were slowly added to the water and dissolved. A 197.2 ppm
internal standard solution of methanol in water was made in a one
liter round bottom flask and set in a cool place. The gas chromatograph was started up and the calculation program was entered. When
the polymer had dissolved, 500 ml of heptane were added under shear
to the process tank. The contaminant solution was made in the feed
tank by dissolving 10.0 ml of toluene in 18.9 liters of water. A
lid was placed on this tank to limit vapor losses. The process tank
was preloaded with 25.0 ml of toluene and the lid was secured. The
appropriate valves were opened, and the process and feed pumps
started. The permeate was returned to the process tank until the
pressure profile was established. Once this was achieved, the permeate was drawn off and its flowrate measured. The contaminant
flowrate was then set equal to the permeate rate and both were
continuously monitored throughout the experiment. The temperature of
the process tank was measured and the coolant temperature setpoint
and flowrate were adjusted until the steady state condition was
obtained. Six one-milliliter samples were taken periodically from
the feed, permeate, and process tank. The clear feed and permeate
samples were capped immediately and labelled. The milky-white

emulsion was capped, labelled and stored in a refrigerator for future
analysis. The aqueous samples were prepared for analysis as soon as
possible. Each sample (2.5 ml) was pipetted into 2.5 ml of internal
standard solution and three to five one-microliter aliquots were
injected into the gas chromatograph.
      The same analysis procedure was used for the two phase mixture.
After the five one-microliter injections into the gas chromatograph,
the elution times began to increase indicating the surfactant polymer was plugging the column. The column was conditioned at 200°C for
two to three hours to remove the polymer.
      The second run followed a similar procedure but used different
quantities of toluene and heptane as indicated in Table I.

Mathematical Model of the Process

During the continuous operation, the toluene concentration in the
heptane increases and it becomes desirable to predict the concentration of toluene in the tank. A material-balance around the system
predicts the toluene concentration in the process tank or the
permeate as a function of time, t, membrane rejection, R, toluene
concentration in feed, C_f, processing rate, Q_p, and tank volume, V.
      An overall material balance on the process tank and the ultra-
filter illustrated in Figure 1, yields Equation 1.

$$Q_f \rho_f - Q_p \rho_p = \rho_e A \frac{dh}{dt} \tag{1}$$

where

Q_f = volumetric flowrate into process tank,
Q_p = volumetric flowrate leaving system,
ρ_f = density of feed,
ρ_p = density of permeate,
ρ_e = density of tank emulsion.
 A = tank area,
 h = liquid height in tank, and
 t = time.

The assumptions inherent in the material balance are:

1. $\rho_f = \rho_p$,
2.   steady state conditions,
3.   process tank is an ideal mixer, and
4.   evaporation losses are neglected.

At steady-state conditions $Q_f = Q_p$ and Equation 1 reduces to:

$$\frac{dV}{dt} = 0 \tag{2}$$

where

$$V = A * h$$

V is the total liquid in the process volume. A toluene material
balance yields:

$$Q_f C_f - Q_p C_p = \frac{V dC}{dt} \tag{3}$$

where

C = toluene concentration in process tank,
C_f = toluene concentration in feed, and
C_p = toluene concentration in permeate.

The membrane rejection coefficient, R, for toluene is measured experimentally and is defined as:

$$R = 1 - \frac{C_p}{C_w} \tag{4}$$

Rearrangement of Equation 4 yields:

$$C_p = (1 - R) C_w \tag{5}$$

C_w is a function of the volume fraction of the two phase mixture and the distribution coefficient and can be derived from Equation 6:

$$C_w V_w + C_h V_h = CV \tag{6}$$

where

C_w = toluene concentration in continuous phase,
V_w = volume of continuous phase,
C_h = toluene concentration in the organic phase,
V_h = volume of organic phase,
C = toluene concentration in process tank, and
V = total liquid volume in process tank.

The distribution coefficient is defined as:

$$D = \frac{C_h}{C_w} \tag{7}$$

Substitution of Equation 7 into Equation 6 yields C_w as:

$$C_w = \frac{CV}{(V_w + DV_h)} \tag{8}$$

Substitution of Equation 8 into Equation 5 yields:

$$C_p = \frac{(1 - R) CV}{(V_w + DV_h)} \tag{9}$$

Finally, if C_p from Equation 9 is substituted into Equation 3, the following first order linear differential equation results:

$$\frac{dC}{dt} + \frac{Q_p C(1-R)}{V_w + DV_h} = \frac{Q_f C_f}{V} \tag{10}$$

This equation can be solved using the integrating factor method, with the initial condition that at $t = 0$, $C = C_o$, the preload concentration of toluene in the process tank. The resulting expression for C is

$$C = \frac{Q_f C_f (V_w + DV_h)}{V Q_p (1 - R)} + \left[C_o - \frac{Q_f C_f (V_w + DV_h)}{V Q_p (1 - R)} \right] e^{-A t} \tag{11}$$

where

$$A = \frac{Q_p \ (1 - R)}{(V_w + DV_h)}$$

If, in addition, the feed rate, Q_f, is set equal to the permeate rate, Q_p, the final expression for the toluene concentration in the process tank is

$$C = \frac{C_f(V_w + DV_h)}{V \ (1 - R)} + \left[C_o - \frac{C_f(V_w + DV_h)}{V \ (1 - R)}\right] Exp\left[- \ Q_p t \ (1-R)/(V_w+DV_h)\right] \quad (12)$$

Equation 12, defines the toluene concentration in the process tank as a function of toluene concentration in the feed, C_f, membrane rejection coefficient, R, total fluid volume in process tank, V, volume of the continuous phase, V_w, volume of the organic phase, V_h, the distribution coefficient, D, time, t, and initial toluene concentration in the process tank, C_o.

Results and Discussion

1. Run Number One. An aqueous stream initially containing 455 ppm of dissolved toluene was pumped into a 10% by volume heptane/water emulsion. The emulsion was then ultrafiltered and the permeate stream showed approximately a ten-fold decrease in toluene concentration over the feed stream value. The inlet and outlet pressures to the ultrafilter, P_1 = 10.0 psig @ P_2 = 0.0 psig, were chosen to minimize membrane fouling while maximizing permeate flux. To aid in the analysis, the heptane/water emulsion was preloaded with 25.0 ml of toluene (7% of the volume of heptane).

The overview of the continuous process shown in Table II displays process flowrates and toluene concentrations over the five hour processing period. During this period, 15.5 liters of contaminated water were processed and approximately 6 ml of toluene were removed. The decrease in process flowrates from 54 ml/min to 50 ml/min was due to membrane fouling. The toluene concentration in the feed tank decreased from 455 ppm to 385 ppm over a five hour interval. These losses were attributed to evaporation of the volatile toluene. The toluene concentration in the permeate increased from 14 ppm to 44 ppm during the run. The toluene concentration in the process tank (both phases) increased from 4162 ppm to 5393 ppm. These results are in agreement with the value of the distribution coefficient of toluene between the heptane and water phases. The toluene concentrations shown in Table II are the averages of the data shown in Figures 2 and 3.

Figures 2 and 3 show the toluene concentration in the feed, permeate and process tank, respectively, as functions of time. The data scatter is more pronounced at higher toluene concentrations because the internal standard method of calculation used the relative response factors which were developed at dilute toluene concentrations (i.e., toluene concentration in permeate). Also, this data scatter could indicate that the gas chromatograph detector response is not linear over the wide range of toluene concentrations examined.

The results of the first order model used to calculate the toluene concentration in the process tank are shown graphically in Figure 3. The prediction by the model is in good agreement with the experimental data. The predicted values were expected to be larger

Table II. Summary of Continuous Extractive-Ultrafiltration
Process in First Continuous Run

Time (Hours)	Feed		Process Tank	Permeate	
	Flow (ml/min)	Concentration* (mg/l)	Concentration* (mg/l)	Flow (ml/min)	Concentration* (mg/l)
0	54	455	4162	54	14
1	53	430	4233	53	23
2	52	412	4742	52	--**
3	50	400	4874	50	35
4	50	390	5027	50	40
5	50	385	5393	50	44

*Concentration of toluene
**Not measured

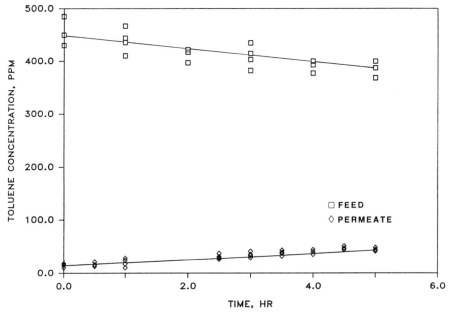

Figure 2. Toluene concentration in the feed and permeate for first continuous run.

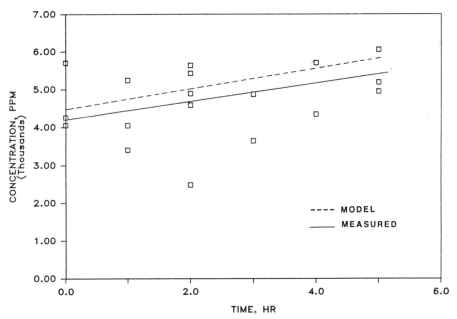

Figure 3. Toluene concentration in the process tank in first continuous run.

than the experimental because losses due to vaporization were not
included in the derivation of the first order model.

2.   Run Number Two.   A 30 percent by volume heptane/water emulsion
was the extraction mixture used in run #2.   The higher heptane concentration offered a larger toluene "sink", and the hydrodynamic
conditions P_1 = 15.0 psig @ P_2 = 2.0 psig increased the contacting
time by lowering the retentate flowrate.   Again, it was desirable
to operate at high permeate and retentate flowrates.   An aqueous
stream containing a 420 ppm level of toluene was pumped to the
process tank at an initial flowrate of 60 ml/min.   The permeate again
showed an approximate ten-fold decrease in concentration.   To aid in
the analysis of the permeate the process tank was preloaded with 113
ml of toluene (7% of the volume of heptane).

   Table III details the process flowrates and concentrations
during the five-hour processing period.   Seventeen liters of a contaminated feed solution were processed and approximately 7 ml of
toluene were extracted during the experiment.   The permeate flux
decrease from 60 ml/min to 55 ml/min was attributed to membrane
fouling.   The toluene concentration in the feed decreased from 420
ppm to 380 ppm.   This fall in concentration was attributed to evaporation.   This 40 ppm loss may be compared to the 70 ppm loss in the
first continuous run.   The difference may be attributed to the 3°C
air temperature change between the two days, which led to a variation in the rate of evaporation of toluene.   The toluene concentration in the permeate increased from 45 ppm to 52 ppm.   In the first
run there was a 30 ppm increase in toluene concentration in the
permeate.   The increase in heptane volume from the run #1 to run #2
is responsible for this difference.   In the first continuous run,
32 ml of toluene were dissolved in the heptane/water emulsion, (500
ml heptane), when the permeate concentration contained 44 ppm of
toluene.   In the second run, 113 ml of toluene were dissolved in the
heptane/water emulsion, (1500 ml heptane), while 45 ppm of toluene
were present in the permeate.   It was more difficult to detect a
change in toluene concentration in the permeate and process tank in
the second continuous experiment compared with the first, because of
the relative differences of toluene to heptane concentration.   The
toluene concentration increased in the process tank by 8% in the
second continuous experiment compared with a 23% increase in the
first continuous run.   In the second continuous run, the toluene
concentration in the process tank increased from 18,128 ppm to
19,723 ppm.

   Figure 4 compares the toluene concentrations in the feed and
permeate as a function of time for the second continuous run.   The
slower rate of increase in the toluene concentration in the permeate
is reflected by the 8% increase in toluene concentration in the
process tank.   Again, as was seen in run #1, the data scatter in
Figure 4 is more obvious in the feed analysis when compared to the
permeate analysis.

   The toluene concentration in the process tank is graphed as a
function of time in Figure 5.   As in run #1, the toluene concentration in the process tank was more scattered than in the feed and
permeate.   The first order model was used to calculate the toluene
concentration in the process tank and its results are in good agreement with the experimental data.   The model predicts higher

Table III.   Summary of Continuous Extractive–Ultrafiltration
Process in Second Continuous Run

Time (Hours)	Feed		Process Tank	Permeate	
	Flow (ml/min)	Concentration* (mg/l)	Concentration* (mg/l)	Flow (ml/min)	Concentration* (mg/l)
0	60	420	18128	60	45
1	58	410	18439	58	47
2	57	406	18776	57	44
3	55	393	19121	55	49
4	55	390	19476	55	54
5	55	380	19723	55	52

*Concentration of toluene.

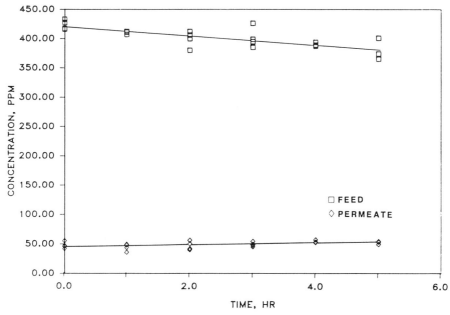

Figure 4. Toluene concentration in the feed and permeate in second continuous run.

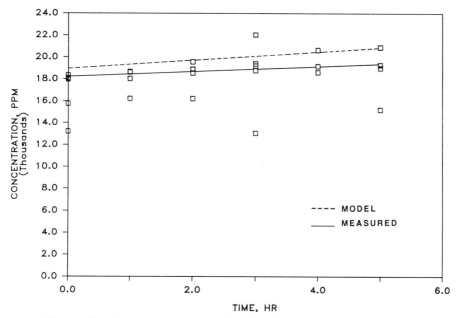

Figure 5. Toluene concentration in the process tank in the second continuous run.

concentrations than the experimentally measured ones because losses due to evaporation of toluene were not included in the model.

Both continuous runs indicate that this continuous extractive-ultrafiltration system can be reasonably modelled using a simple first-order expression.

Conclusions

1. In both continuous extractive-ultrafiltration experiments, over a ten-fold decrease in toluene concentration was seen between the feed and the permeate.
2. A first-order expression can be used to model this particular continuous extractive-ultrafiltration system.
3. The polymeric-surfactant, PEO/PVA, severely fouls the polysulphone membeane, in effect forming a dynamic membrane. The transmembrane flux is thus substantially reduced from the optimum value.
4. A combination of backflushing and cleaning by total recycle with a dilute sodium hypochlorite solution effectively restores membrane flux.

Acknowledgments

The authors wish to thank the Graduate School at the University of Louisvilel for the purchase of the ultrafiltration system. We are also indebted to Dr. D. J. Collins for his assistance with the GC analysis.

Notation

A	=	cross-section of tank
C	=	toluene concentration in process tank
C_f	=	toluene concentration in feed
C_h	=	toluene concentration in organic phase
C_o	=	initial toluene loading in process tank
C_p	=	toulene concentration in permeate
C_w	=	toluene concentration in the water phase
D	=	distribution coefficient for toluene between organic and water phases
h	=	height of liquid in process tank
PHYD	=	hydrodynamic pressure
P_1	=	inlet pressure to ultrafilter (Psig)
P_2	=	outlet pressure from ultrafilter, retentate side (Psig)
Q_f	=	volumetric flow rate of feed into process tank
Q_p	=	volumetric flow rate of permeate from system
R	=	rejection coefficient of membrane for toluene
t	=	time
V	=	total volume of liquid in process tank
V_h	=	total volume of organic phase in process tank
V_w	=	total volume of aqueous phase in process tank
ρ_e	=	density of emulsion
ρ_f	=	density of feed
ρ_p	=	density of permeate

Literature Cited

1. Hwang, S. T. and Fahrenthold, P.; "Treatability of the Organic Priority Pollutants by Steam Stripping," AIChE Symp. Ser., Vol. 76, No. 37, 37-60, 1980.
2. Keith, L. H. and Telliard, W. A.; "Priority Pollutants: I--A Perspective View," Environ. Sci. and Tech., Vol. 13, No. 4, 1979.
3. Dowd, R. M. "EPA Drinking-Water Proposals: Round Two," Environ. Sci. Technol., Vol. 20, No. 1, 1986.
4. Barbarl, T. A. and King, C. J.; "Equilibrium Distribution Coefficients for Extraction of Chlorinated Hydrocarbons and Aromatics from Water into Undecane," Environ. Sci. Technol., Vol. 16, No. 9, 624-627, 1982.
5. Bhattacharyya, D.; Jumawan, A. B.; and Grieves, R. B.; "Ultrafiltration Characteristics of Oil-Detergent-Water Systems: Membrane Fouling Mechanisms," Separation Science and Technology, Vol. 14, No. 6, 529-549, 1979. TP156.S45A1.54
6. Bhattacharyya, D.; Garrison, K. A.; and Grieves, R. B.; "Membrane Ultrafiltration: Waste Treatment Application for Water Reuse," Proc. Ind. Waste Conf., Vol. 30, 120-131, 1975.
7. Bhattacharyya, D., Garrison, K. A.; Jumawan, A. B.; and Grieves, R. B.; "Membrane Ultrafiltration of a Nonionic Surfactant and Inorganic Salts from Complex Aqueous Suspensions: Design for Water Reuse," AIChE Journal, Vol. 21, No. 6, 1057-1065, 1975.
8. Abcor Inc., U. S. Patent 1,456,304; November 24, 1976.
9. Beaton, N. C. and Hasleden, J. D.; U. S. Patent 1,475, 745; June 1, 1977.
10. Benzinger, W. D.; Parekh, B. S.; and Eichelberger, J. L.; "Ultrafiltration with Kynar Poly (Vinylidiene Flouride) Membranes," Separation Science and Technology, Vol. 15, No. 4, 1193-1204, 1980.
11. Hekal, I. M., U. S. Patent 4,201,664; May 6, 1980. TP159.M4.J681
12. Lee, S.; Aurelle, Y.; and Rogues, H.; "Concentration Polarization: Membrane Fouling and Cleaning in Ultrafiltration of Soluble Oil, "Journal of Membrane Science, Vol. 19, 23-38, 1984.
13. Modolo, R. and Vittori, P.; "Hydrodynamic Behavior of Water-Tri-n-butylphosphate Emulsions during Ultrafiltration," Separation Science and Technology, Vol. 19, 297-306, 1984.
14. Tanny, G. B. and Hauk, D.; "Filtration of Particulates and Emulsions with a Pleated, Thin Channel, Cross-Flow Module," Separation Science and Technology, Vol. 15, 317-337, 1980.
15. Tanny, G. B., "Dynamic Membranes in Ultrafiltration and Reverse Osmosis," Sep. Purif. Methods, Vol. 7, No. 2, 183-220, 1978.
16. Mackay, D. and Shin, Wan-Ying; "The Aqueous Solubility and Air-Water Exchange Characteristics of Hydrocarbons under Environmental Conditions," Chemistry and Physics of Aqueous Gas Solutions, ASTM, Philadelphia, Pa., 104-198, 1974.
17. Murrer, D. G., "The Selective Removal of a Trace Organic Contaminant from an Aqueous Stream by Extractive Ultrafiltration," M.Eng. thesis, University of Louisville, Louisville, KY, May 1986.

RECEIVED January 9, 1987

Chapter 13

Actinide Removal from Aqueous Waste Using Solid Supported Liquid Membranes

Anthony C. Muscatello, James D. Navratil[1], and Marlene Y. Price

Rockwell International, Rocky Flats Plant, Golden, CO 80402-0464

The actinides americium and plutonium can be removed
and recovered from nitrate-nitric acid waste solutions
using solid supported liquid membranes. The bifunctional organophosphorus extractants dihexyl-N,-
N-diethylcarbamoylmethylphosphonate (DHDECMP) and
octylphenyl-N,N-diisobutylcarbamoylmethylphosphine
oxide (OØD(iB)CMPO) effectively remove actinides from
low acid-high nitrate conditions when supported on
Accurel polypropylene hollow fibers. Studies of the
sorption of americium on inorganic ion exchangers from
0.25$\underline{M}$ oxalic acid and water are included to demonstrate
the feasibility of actinide concentration from the
strip solution after membrane transfer.

Our research program at Rocky Flats has been aimed at reducing the
levels of americium and plutonium in the nitric acid waste which
arises from the anion exchange purification of plutonium. These
wastes currently contain TRU or transuranic elements to such a
concentration that the waste must be stored in a geological
repository after neutralization and flocculant precipitation. Table
I shows the average composition of the waste.

Reducing the plutonium level to 10^{-5} g/l and americium to 10^{-7}
g/l would allow production of a sludge which can be stored as
low-level waste. In addition, economic considerations and radiation
exposure limits also favor reduction of plutonium to 10^{-5} g/l and
americium to $<10^{-5}$ g/l.

One promising technique to accomplish this task is solid
supported liquid membrane (SLM) transfer using new extractants that
are selective for actinides of various valencies ([1,2]). Our
previous work ([3]), also has demonstrated the utility of this
technique and is reviewed and extended in this paper.

---

[1]Current address: Colorado School of Mines, Department of Chemistry and
Geochemistry, Golden, CO 80401

Table I. Composition of Rocky Flats Waste Nitric Acid

Component	Concentration
HNO_3	7.5$\underline{M}$
Pu	1.0×10^{-3} g/l
Am	6.6×10^{-3} g/l
$Mg(NO_3)_2$	39 g/l
$Fe(NO_3)_3$	0.54 g/l
$Al(NO_3)_3$	0.25 g/l
$Ca(NO_3)_2$	0.30 g/l

Simply defined in this context, a SLM is a device for selectively removing metal ions from one aqueous phase and delivering them
to another aqueous phase. Danesi et al. (1,4), have thoroughly
studied the chemistry, kinetics, and operation of SLM and we wish to
apply this knowledge to our system as well as solve the problem of
the disposal of the recovered actinides. One method to accomplish
the latter goal is to sorb the metal ion from the strip solution
onto an inorganic cation exchanger. Consequently, we have also
investigated the distribution ratios of americium for several
candidate materials.

Experimental

Materials. DHDECMP [$(C_6H_{11}O)_2P(O)CH_2C(O)N(C_2H_5)_2$] was produced as
an acid-free, 84 vol% pure liquid by Bray Oil Co. OØD(iB)CMPO
[$(C_8H_{17})(C_6H_5)P(O)CH_2C(O)N$ (iso-$C_4H_9)_2$] was obtained as a 98% pure
solid material from M & T Chemicals, Inc. Dowex 50WX8 resin
(50-100 mesh) was supplied by Dow Chemical Co. Reagent grade TBP
[$(C_4H_9O)_3P(O)$] was purchased from Eastman Kodak.
    Table II summarizes the inorganic ion exchangers and their
relevant properties and suppliers.
    Purified americium and plutonium were obtained from Rocky Flats
production operations. Water was distilled and deionized. All
other materials used were reagent grade.

Procedures. Americium transfer behavior was studied using hollow
fiber membrane modules assembled in the laboratory. Each module
consisted of two Armak Accurel hollow fibers, each 11.5 cm long and
0.15 cm i.d. with a 0.1 cm wall thickness, sealed into a glass tube
14 cm long x 0.8 cm i.d. by using RTV silicone adhesive. The hollow
fibers have a nominal void volume of 75%. The glass tube is
equipped with side inlet and outlet ports.
    The decrease in americium concentration in the feed solution as
a function of time was monitored with an on-line NaI(Tl) gamma
detector and a Canberra Series 35 multichannel analyzer operating in
the multiscalar mode. Most experiments were run with a dwell-time
of 1 min., allowing >17 hours of continuous observation. The
detector was calibrated by the use of solutions containing known
amounts of americium.

The feed and strip solutions were circulated through the module using Cole-Parmer Master-Flex tubing pumps. Unless otherwise noted,

Table II. Inorganic Ion Exchangers

Exchanger	Grade	Supplier
Zirconium phosphate	"for research only"	Pfaltz & Bauer
Zirconium tungstate	technical	Alfa
Sodium titanate	–	R. G. Dosch, Sandia Nat'l Lab.
Ferrite	magnetite	Pfizer
Peatmoss	acid treated	(from Glenamoy, Co. Mayo, Ireland)
Alumina	150 mesh activated	Aldrich
Bone char	calcium phosphate	Stauffer Chemical Co.

flow rates were maintained at 10 ml/min. The initial and final americium concentrations were also determined radiometrically. Uncertainties in the data are estimated to be 5-10%.

Distribution ratio experiments with inorganic cation exchangers were performed by equilibrating 1.0 g of the exchanger with 10 ml of either 0.25$\underline{M}$ oxalic acid or water in a 14 ml vial on a rotating wheel for up to 72 hours. The aqueous pH was adjusted with 50% NaOH or 7$\underline{M}$ HNO$_3$. The initial and final americium and plutonium concentrations were determined radiometrically. The volume distribution ratio, D, is defined as [Am]/g solid ÷ [Am]/ml aqueous phase and is calculated from 10 x ([Am]aq^{initial} - [Am]aq^{final}/[Am]aq^{final}).

Permeability Calculations. Danesi et al. (5) derived the following equation to calculate the permeability (P_m) of the metal ion through the membrane:

$$Ln \frac{[M]_o}{[M]_t} = \frac{P_m At}{V}$$ (1)

where:

$[M]_o$ = Feed concentration at time zero,

$[M]_t$ = Feed concentration at time t,

A = Surface area of the membrane,

t = Time, and

V = Volume of cell.

A plot of the left hand side of Equation 1 versus time gives a straight line whose slope is $P_m A/V$.

Results and Discussion

Effect of Nitric Acid. Preliminary experiments showed incomplete transfer of americium from 7.0M nitric acid through a membrane of undiluted DHDECMP to 0.25M oxalic acid. Danesi et al. (2) have shown that such membranes also transport nitric acid. Consequently, the nitric acid concentration of the strip solution increases with time and the driving force of the transfer, the nitrate concentration gradient, is neutralized. When this occurs, equilibrium is reached and no further net changes in americium concentration are observed. See Horwitz et al. (6) for the equations describing the chemistry of the extraction.

To counteract the effect, experiments were performed with decreasing amounts of nitric acid mixed with sodium nitrate to simulate partial neutralization of the acid waste. Table III summarizes the results of this study.

Table III.   Transfer of Americium(III) Through a DHDECMP Membrane on Accurel Hollow Fibers. (Initial $[Am]=10^{-4}$ g/1)

$[HNO_3]$,M	$[NaNO_3]$,M	% Transfer	$10^{-4} \dfrac{Pm}{cm\ sec^{-1}}$
7.0	0.0	61	—
5.0	2.0	64	—
3.0	4.0	76	—
1.0	6.0	90	—
0.1	6.9	94	7.2

Source: Reproduced with permission from Ref. 9. Copyright 1987, Marcel Dekker.

The feed volume was 50 ml and the strip volume was 15 ml. The net membrane area was 8.0 cm^2. Smooth curves were observed for plots according to Equation 1 with increasing americium transfer with decreasing nitric acid concentration and a constant total nitrate concentration of 7.0M. Only at 0.1M nitric acid is there sufficient transfer to allow the fitting of a straight line to the data. The calculated permeability is listed in Table II. This value for americium, 7.2 x 10^{-4} cm/sec, is about twice that measured by Danesi et al.(2) from 1.0M nitric acid, using a 430 micron thick Accurel hollow-fiber loaded with 0.25M OØD(iB)CMPO plus 0.75M TBP in decalin.

Thus, the best condition of those tested for americium transfer is 0.1M nitric acid plus 6.9M sodium nitrate. Actual Rocky Flats waste streams may be brought to these conditions by titration with the appropriate amount of sodium hydroxide. A similar study of the transfer of plutonium (IV), using the same conditions shows a similar permeability, but the fraction transfered is lower (70%). A possible explanation for lower transfer of plutonium may be the transport of oxalic acid into the feed solution from the strip solution by DHDECMP. The oxalic acid then in the feed would strongly complex the plutonium (IV), preventing its complete extraction by the carrier. Americium (III) would not be noticeably affected by the oxalic acid.

Effect of Feed to Strip Ratio. Further experiments were performed to investigate the effect of feed-to-strip (F:S) ratio on americium transfer and to evaluate the possibility of concentrating the metal ions simultaneously with removal. A linear relationship would be expected between the F:S ratio and the concentration factor, the ratio of the final strip concentration divided by the initial feed concentration assuming no complications arise. However, the results shown in Table IV indicate the actual concentration factor is much less than the F:S ratio, possibly because a large fraction of the americium is held in the membrane at the conclusion of the run. In addition, the relationship between the ratio and the percent transferred is roughly inverse because of the increased amount of nitric acid transferred into the strip solution with larger feed volumes.

Table IV. Effect of Feed:Strip Volume Ratio on Americium Transfer from 7.0$\underline{M}$ HNO_3 to 0.25$\underline{M}$ $H_2C_2O_4$ Through a DHDECMP SLM (Initial [Am] $= 10^{-3}$ g/l)

Feed Volume, ml	Strip Volume, ml	Volume Ratio	% Transfer	Conc. Factor
50	15	3.33:1	80	0.90
50	10	5:1	52	0.62
150	15	10:1	45	0.58

Source: Reproduced with permission from Ref. 9. Copyright 1987, Marcel Dekker.

Cation Exchange of the Strip Solution. In order to improve the somewhat disappointing results given above for the concentration factor, and to convert the americium into a discardable form, the strip solution was circulated through a column of cation exchange resin, Dowex 50WX8, placed in series with the membrane module. Table V shows the results of this study.

Table V. Americium Transfer and Sorption with the Combined DHDECMP Membrane/Cation Exchange System

Solution	Run	Volume, ml	Initial [Am],g/l	Final [Am],g/l	Transfer, %	Equilibrium Time, min.
Feed	1	75	8.0×10^{-4}	1.5×10^{-4}	82	342
Strip	1	15	0	$<4.1 \times 10^{-6}$	–	
Feed	2	150	8.0×10^{-4}	1.9×10^{-4}	76	1510
Strip	2	30	0	$<4.1 \times 10^{-6}$	–	

Source: Reproduced with permission from Ref. 9. Copyright 1987, Marcel Dekker.

The feeds were 6.9$\underline{M}$ $NaNO_3$ + 0.1$\underline{M}$ HNO_3 and the strips were 0.25$\underline{M}$ oxalic acid. The resin bed weighed 0.87g. For both runs, the final americium concentration is less than the detection limit of our radiochemical laboratory, indicating that the resin efficiently

removes any americium in the strip solution and concentrates it
greatly. The increased time to equilibrium in Run 2 is consistent
with Equation 1 since the feed volume is greater. Another advantage
of the combined system is that it reduces the amount of americium
held up on the membrane since back transfer is greatly reduced.

A practical americium removal and disposal system can be based
on these results. Instead of the difficult to discard organic resin
Dowex 50WX8, an inorganic ion exchanger can be used which would sorb
all the selectively transferred americium from the strip solution
which could then be recycled. The inorganic material would then be
dried, shielded, and packaged to become a safe material for long
term waste storage in a geologic repository.

Evaluation of Inorganic Ion Exchangers. The materials in Table II
were evaluated for their ability to sorb americium from both 0.25M
oxalic acid and water, each adjusted to an initial pH of 1.0. High
distribution ratios under these conditions are essential to
accomplish the immobilization and disposal of americium.

Data were collected until equilibrium was achieved for all the
materials. However, a more operational value for the distribution
ratio, D, is that for a one hour contact time, simulating a
production environment where time is very valuable. Table VI lists
the distribution ratios for some of the materials from 0.25M oxalic
acid.

Table VI.   Volume Distribution Ratios for Selected Ion Exchangers
            from 0.25M Oxalic Acid After a One-Hour Contact at pH - 1.0

Material	D	Final pH
Sodium Titanate	540	4.4
Zirconium Tungstate	5.2	2.2
Zirconium Phosphate	5.2	2.0
Dowex 50WX8	36	1.0
Alumina	250	1.0
Ferrite	1.2	3.0
Peatmoss	5.4	2.0

Obviously, the best candidates are sodium titanate and alumina,
based on their D values being much higher than those of Dowex 50WX8,
shown above to be adequate. The sorption of americium and plutonium
from oxalic acid by alumina has been demonstrated previously (7).
The D-value is consistent with the previously observed trend of
higher sorption at lower nitric acid concentration.

To avoid any possibility of the precipitation of americium (III)
oxalate from the strip solution and to eliminate the transfer of
oxalic acid into the feed, it could be replaced with water. To
determine the effect of such a change, D-values were obtained for
water as well. The results are shown in Table VII.

Again, sodium titanate has the highest D-values, but all the
candidate materials except ferrite have high D-values from this
noncomplexing medium. In such a case, great latitude is available
in selecting a material and other considerations, such as price,

availability, and physical characteristics can determine the choice
of material.

For both media, pH changes occurred since none of the material
had been preconditioned and the solutions were not buffered.
Consequently, some caution should be exercised in this comparison,
but the data are useful in a screening program such as ours.

Table VII.   Volume Distribution Ratios for Selected Inorganic Ion
              Exchangers from 0.10M HNO$_3$ After a One-Hour Contact

Material	D	Final pH
Sodium Titanate	3500	6.8
Zirconium Tungstate	790	3.0
Zirconium Phosphate	1100	5.0
Bone Char	570	6.8
Ferrite	0.8	1.0

Transfer by OØD(iB)CMPO Plus TBP. In light of the better hydrolytic
and radiolytic properties, superior availability, and large volume
of supporting data of OØD(iB)CMPO (8), we also studied the transfer
of americium through a membrane of 0.25M OØD(iB)CMPO plus 0.75M TBP
in decalin from a simulated waste of the composition given in
Table I into water. However, plutonium was omitted. The results of
this series of experiments are assembled in Table VIII.

Table VIII.   Transfer of Americium Through Hollow Fiber Membranes of
              0.25M OØD(iB)CMPO + 0.75M TBP in Decalin; t = 17 hr.

Run	Flow Rate, ml/min. Feed		Feed [H$^+$], M	% Americium Transferred
	Feed	Strip		
1	9	0.2	7.5	8.7
2	9	0.2	0.1	45
3	100	0.2	0.1	52
4	100	100	0.1	54

1.0 1 Feed (See Table I for composition.)
0.1 1 Strip (H$_2$O)

These experiments were allowed to run for only 17 hours, again
to simulate a production environment. In all cases, the transfer
was at or close to equilibrium at the end of this time.

The four runs illustrate our attempts to maximize americium
transfer with this extractant. Run 1 shows very little transfer for
this 10:1 F:S ratio at 7.5M acidity and a flow rate of the strip
solution designed to allow it to pass through the module only once,
without recirculation. This was done to try to minimize the effect
of transferred nitric acid.

Run 2 shows a dramatic increase in % transferred occurs upon
neutralization to 0.1M acidity, whereas increasing the flow rate of
the feed by more than ten-fold (Run 3), has very little additional
affect. Furthermore, recycling and increasing the flow rate of the

strip solution (Run 4), has only a slight positive effect on the transfer. Apparently, the slow, single pass strip solution condition is not effective and is not necessary.

Although the amount of americium transfer is somewhat less than desired for an operational system, these experiments show the feasibility of using SLM to remove and concentrate actinides from nitrate waste solutions. Improvements would come from increased membrane surface area and better complexing agents in the strip solution. Insertion of the inorganic ion exchanger into the strip circuit would also improve the process performance.

Summary

We have investigated the transfer of americium and, to some extent, plutonium from aqueous nitrate wastes using supported liquid membranes of the bifunctional organophosphorus extractants DHDECMP and O∅D(iB)CMPO (+TBP). The results show good transfer and removal if the nitric acid in the feed is first neutralized to $0.10\underline{M}$ to minimize acid transfer and subsequent back transfer of the metal ion.

In addition, we have also demonstrated the removal of the actinide from the strip solution and its concentration on an ion exchanger. We have identified candidate inorganic ion exchangers that would allow sorption and direct disposal of americium in a waste repository.

Research and development are still necessary to answer questions about the lifetime of SLM and to optimize actinide transfer results, but our studies have demonstrated the great potential benefits of this technique.

Literature Cited

1.   Danesi, P. R.; Horwitz, E. P.; and Rickert, P. G. J. Phys. Chem. 1983, 87, 4708.
2.   Danesi, P. R.; Chiarizia, R.; Rickert, P.; and Horwitz, E. P. Solvent Extr. Ion Exch. 1985, 3, 111.
3.   Muscatello, A. C.; Navratil, J. D.; Killion, M. E.; and Price, M. Y. Sep. Sci. Technol. 1987, 22, 305.
4.   Danesi, P. R. J. Membrane Sci. 1984, 20, 231.
5.   Danesi, P. R.; Horwitz, E. P.; Vandegrift, G. F.; and Chiarizia, R. Sep. Sci. Technol. 1981, 16, 201.
6.   Horwitz, E. P.; Muscatello, A. C.; Kalina, D. G. and Kaplan, L. Sep. Sci. Technol. 1981, 16, 417.
7.   Subba Rao, M.; Gaikwad, A. M.; Rao, V. K.; and Natarajan, P. R. Sep. Sci. Technol. 1985, 20, 205.
8.   Vandegrift, G. F.; Leonard, R. A.; Steindler, M. J.; Horwitz, E. P.; Basile, L. J.; Diamond, H.; Kalina, D. G.; and Kaplan, L. Report ANL-84-45 1984, U. S. Dept. of Energy, Argonne, IL.
9.   Sep. Sci. Technol. Special Issue 1987, 22(2,3), 843-845.

RECEIVED March 13, 1987

INDEXES

Author Index

Affiliation Index

Subject Index

Production and indexing by Janet S. Dodd
Jacket design by Carla L. Clemens

Elements typeset by Hot Type Ltd., Washington, DC
Book printed and bound by Maple Press Co., York, PA
Dust jackets printed by Atlantic Research Corporation, Alexandria, VA

Recent ACS Books